Gibbard's

DOUBLE DECADE
OMNIBUS

'Good luck, kid — and by the way, there don't seem to be any brakes!'

DOUBLE DECADE
OMNIBUS

Modern History in Political Cartoons, 1969-91

Edited and Introduced by
Les Gibbard

BELLEW PUBLISHING
London

OTHER TITLES IN THE CARTOON LIBRARY
(General Editor: Mark Bryant)

The Complete Colonel Blimp edited by Mark Bryant
(Foreword by Rt Hon. Michael Foot MP, Introduction by Colin Seymour-Ure)

JON's Complete Two Types edited and introduced by JON
(Foreword by Lord Cudlipp)

The Last Bohemian: G. L. Stampa of Punch
edited and introduced by Flavia Stampa Gruss
(Foreword by David Thomas)

First published in Great Britain in 1991 by
Bellew Publishing Company Limited
7 Southampton Place, London WC1A 2DR

ISBN 0 947792 83 X

Printed and bound in Great Britain by Hartnolls Limited

CONTENTS

PREFACE

Cartooning mythology has it that the giants of political cartooning constantly made their readers gnash their teeth, reach for their fountain pens, and threaten to cancel their subscriptions. An explanation is that an enlightened and mischievous proprietor like Beaverbook didn't think it hurt to wake his slumbering readership with leftish political cartoons in direct conflict with right-wing editorials. It made things more interesting and controversial — and it sold newspapers.

Today, I'm afraid, we political cartoonists tend to preach to the converted. It's no secret that I oppose most Tory policy but my worst backlashes have been from militant lefties, sneering at my wimpishness in not graphically hanging, drawing and quartering every Tory cabinet minister.

As a respected quality liberal newspaper (veering occasionally to the left), the *Guardian* has fought a sometimes lonely fight against the excesses of the Thatcher years, and is required reading at Westminster, even among Tory cabinet ministers who take cartoon lampooning in good cheer.

'You have never yet portrayed me in a cartoon in any way that suggests you agree with me,' says Kenneth Clarke, the genial bully of health-workers and teachers. 'You have, however, cartooned me so effectively that I have collected a number of originals and put them on fairly prominent display in my home!' 'The only cartoonist that really offends is the one that excludes one totally,' adds Michael Heseltine. 'Gibbard has never punished me that severely!'

Cabinet ministers may read the *Guardian* but not many Tory voters do. It therefore follows that no matter how clever a cartoon may have been and how irrefutable its logic, it has never made one iota of difference to the outcome of a poll.

But at last comes a chance to reach a wider audience, and, who knows, some may be Tory voters! This collection of 22 years of *Guardian* cartoons also responds to many requests over the period from loyal readers, one of whom wouldn't accept that a book didn't exist and placed a firm order with a bookshop just in case.

To whittle down an encyclopedia's worth of modern historic events to one small volume has not been easy. It is tempting to choose only the well-drawn cartoons, but news has a distressing tendency to break at the last minute, so many of my most significant comments have been drawn in half an hour or less — and may look it.

We all have short memories. Even a supposedly professional political commentator must rush to the files to explain to himself why an issue was a matter of life or death just a couple of years ago. Of course politicians thrive on the public's collective amnesia, together with their distaste for reading learned tomes which might bring it all back. The image a good cartoon can brand on the memory is not so easy to erase.

My own knowledge of twentieth-century history owes a lot to images bequeathed by David Low. As a boy I'd often curl up with a volume of his cartoons in a summer-holiday 'pup' tent away from the merciless antipodean sun and flies, preferring the company of long-gone world leaders to crayfish-red skin. Winter Sundays provided the opportunity to sit alone in the echoing Auckland public library, dressed in school uniform for lack of anything better, poring through an almost complete collection of his works. There was no doubt which career I wished to pursue.

If Mrs Thatcher achieved nothing else in 11 and a half years, she did impose dogma and politics on every aspect of everyday life. No man, woman or mature child can be oblivious to politics any more, even if it is only to wonder in shell-shocked fashion what hit us.

Hopefully this book will help to nudge the memory.

My warmest thanks to the BBC's political editor and *Guardian* old boy John Cole for writing the Foreword — 'That's easy, Les, all you're asking for is a history of the twentieth century, isn't it?' I am indebted to Ib Bellew for recognizing the publishing possibilities, Bob Vickers for his design skills, and a man with a prodigious appetite for facts on cartoons and cartoonists — Mark Bryant — for editing the opus. The staff of Kall Kwik in Chiswick went through hell xeroxing hundreds of originals down to manageable size, and my wife Susannah was my sounding-board, adviser, and endured my little ways as I sifted through tin trunks of cartoons and cuttings. Thanks all. And above all to the *Guardian*, without whom . . .

Les Gibbard
London, 1991

FOREWORD: JOHN COLE

Les Gibbard's cartoons for the *Guardian* span a turbulent quarter-of-a-century. In the world, it has seen a freezing and a thaw of the East—West relationship, followed by break-up of the Communist empire; war in Vietnam; frequent famine in Africa. In Europe, we have witnessed what the ballroom-dancing generation called a fox-trot — slow, slow, quick, quick, slow — evolution of the Community, with Britain often treading, deliberately or not, on its partners' toes.

And Britain itself? We have continued to do what an American statesman accused us of a generation ago: lost an empire, and not yet decided whether our new role is Atlanticist or European or, more sensibly, both. At home, we have continued to struggle with an irritable economy, tried several ideologies, and found them wanting, and wavered between having strong leaders and being 'comfortable with ourselves'. At the time of writing, we are still not sure which we want.

When Les arrived from New Zealand, I was News Editor of the *Guardian*, where I had made landfall — another outsider — a dozen or more years earlier. His approach to the news desk, a newspaper's stock-exchange of ideas, was less per-emptory than that of his predecessor, William Papas, who would demand: 'Hi, John, what's news?' Les is a gentle giant, and preferred to take information in through the pores. The results, from both men, were drawings which we words-miths could only envy. I passed on to the *Observer*, and then to broadcasting, but

Les and I have happily resumed our partnership in a cartoon-based political column for *On the Record*, BBC Television's Sunday-lunchtime programme.

The political pendulum swung frantically in the earlier period covered by this book. Les had to perform a late-night 'head job' on his jack-in-the-box when Harold Wilson lost the 1970 Election, a result everybody except Ted Heath thought impossible. Heath's brief premiership was notable for Britain's entry, after long travail, much of it self-imposed, into the European Community. That was his finest hour, but it all ended in tears after the 1973 miners' strike produced three-day-week working in industry. The Conservatives went to the country in February 1974 on a 'Who governs?' ticket, and received the brusque answer: 'Not you.' Ted Heath's courtship of Jeremy Thorpe over the weekend of defeat was a harbinger of much pipe-dreaming during the next couple of decades about what we would do — by 'we' I mean the Queen, you, I and the politicians — if a general election produced a hung Parliament, and much happy musing in the Centre of politics about how much more often Britain would have hung — or 'balanced' — Parliaments if they were elected under a system of proportional representation.

Harold Wilson gave his answer by forming a minority government. When he appealed to the voters again for an overall majority in October 1974, an increasingly desperate Ted Heath tried to interest them in GNU, a Government of National Unity, but was rejected again, with fatal consequences for his own political career. The concept of a Businessmen's Government had a wider circulation, though this was a fashion, as so often in politics, that passed quickly once the 'Britain is ungovernable' panic subsided.

The Wilson Government, like its predecessor, had a bumpy economic ride until its leader handed over to Jim Callaghan in 1976. By that time, Margaret Thatcher had challenged and defeated Heath for the Conservative leadership. On the Opposition side of politics, a radical revolution had begun whose scope was little suspected. Most people were just astonished that the Tories were the first party in a major Western democracy to be led by a woman. So were most senior Tories.

Jim Callaghan, wartime Navy man, tried to maintain a steady-as-she-goes course through turbulent waters. The weakness of sterling famously forced his Chancellor of the Exchequer, Denis Healey, to turn back at Heathrow Airport from an intended journey to America. He lectured the Labour Party Conference on the Facts of Life (economic, not sexual). Soon Britain was in painful negotiations with the International Monetary Fund, and the Labour Government sadly accepted cuts in public services that represented the shape of things to come. With its majority eroded, the Government made a pact with David Steel's Liberals, the only example of inter-party co-operation to sustain a government since Churchill's wartime coalition with Labour and Liberals broke up in 1945.

It was the trade unions' unwillingness, or inability, to sustain Jim Callaghan's pay policy that produced the Winter of Discontent, a disruption of public services which savagely reminded voters of the conflict that had made them turn Ted Heath out of office five years earlier. The received wisdom is that if Callaghan had been wise enough — or sly enough — to call an election before that winter, he might have won. There is precious little evidence to support this.

Before we consider Margaret Thatcher's 11-and-a-half years in power, I should warn readers that Les Gibbard's book includes a not-so-plain man's guide to the political economy of Britain in these years. Fortunately this will make you laugh, which saves you from crying. That might be the result if you just considered the course of events as described in a million editorial articles that I and others have penned. Perhaps we all worry too much. Britain remains, terrorism and occasional racial intolerance aside, a pleasant place to live. So what if we do not Sincerely Want to be Rich?

The problem about that argument is that we do not, on the other hand, sincerely want to be poor, cannot reconcile ourselves to having a constant shrinkage of our once mighty manufacturing industry, mounting unemployment, declining standards of living and public services. So the 'British disease' — variously attributed during this quarter-century to stop-go economic policies by governments, lack of enterprise among managers, or bloody-mindedness by trade unionists — has become a national obsession and, as the cartoons demonstrate, peeps its ugly face into the political debate as year succeeds year.

The longer I study politics, the more I realize that it is an occupation susceptible to fashion. Just as skirt lengths go up or down, as Paris, London, Milan or New York decrees, so John Maynard Keynes giveth and Milton Friedman taketh away. But without drowning the reader in the technicalities of the Dismal Science, it is possible to discern the underlying dilemma from which successive governments have steered away, until their noses, yet again, are bumped against it.

Britain's economic weakness in the post-war period can be simply defined: we have not been able to achieve the industrial growth we need to maintain the living standards and public services our people demand, without running into an inflation that forces governments to slam the brakes on growth. Hence, stop-go. During the period this book covers, we have seen this phenomenon under Harold Wilson ('I'm the family doctor — leave it to me'); Edward Heath ('Something has got to be done'); Jim Callaghan ('Keep calm'), Margaret Thatcher ('No turning back'), and now John Major. Before that, it occurred under Attlee, Churchill, Eden, Macmillan, and Douglas-Home.

Both Conservative and Labour governments have sought the Holy Grail, 'growth without inflation', by many routes. Most have tiptoed, or galumphed, through the labour market, that uncharted jungle in which only personnel officers of businesses and trade-union negotiators possess one kind of expertise, while economic advisers to governments — not to speak of economic pundits in journalism — have quite a different expertise. Each is contemptuous of the other, which does not help understanding: as if the cardiologist and the abdominal surgeon despised each other's knowledge of a patient.

Two broad assumptions have been made about a cure for labour-market weakness. One is that some kind of consensus among government, employers and unions is needed. This has been variously called a 'national plan', 'incomes policy', 'guiding light', 'social contract': you name it, or rather they do, each successive generation of ministers struggling in Laocoon-like perpetuity with this apparently invincible monster. Labour governments in the past have tried this course with temporary, but no sign of permanent, success. Neil Kinnock is deeply suspicious of it. On the Conservative side, so was Ted Heath, but in the end he tried it too, and again achieved only temporary relief from his troubles.

The principal alternative course, favoured during the Thatcher years, has been to attack what are stigmatized as labour-market rigidities and distortions. This, broadly speaking, means trade-union restrictive practices, national pay bargaining and, among the more doctrinaire, collective bargaining itself. Again, the theory, or parts of it, have had a long history. They were flirted with by Harold Wilson and Barbara Castle in their White Paper for changing the labour market, 'In Place of Strife'; attempted by Ted Heath, in his abortive Industrial Relations Act and Court; bulldozed through by Margaret Thatcher in a succession of laws restricting the activities of unions.

The current fashion among politicians is to deride incomes policies as even one weapon in the fight against inflation. The usual, scornful response to any suggestion that they will have to be tried again one day is: 'They don't work.' Few notice that, for this problem, nothing has worked. The anti-union legislation of the last decade was once supposed to have taken the sting out of wage inflation. But such claims were made during the recession of the early and mid Eighties, when union negotiators, as always during recessions, did not push their luck.

What was remarkable about the Thatcher years is how quickly, as growth returned in the Lawson Boom of the late Eighties, the unions got their skates on again. The market contained a willing seller and a willing buyer of labour, and the unions saw no reason for restraint. They were not the *initiators* of the recent disastrous inflation, which has produced the second recession of the Thatcher era, with unemployment again rising towards levels unprecedented since the Thirties. What they did do, once inflation was already raging, was to refuse to respond to ministers' exhortations to restrain their demands: there was no machinery to ensure that such restraint would be reflected elsewhere, so they could not see how it would bring benefits to the workers they represented.

The obduracy of this problem has recently produced a third proposed remedy, a new emphasis, on both sides of the political fence, on education and training. Britain, it is now said, lags far behind other industrial countries in equipping its people with the skills needed to compete in the modern world: that is why our manufacturing has been defeated in international markets, and is growing ever smaller. This current anxiety about manufacturing, incidentally, is a reaction to the view a few years ago, once sedulously argued by Mrs Thatcher, that Britain's future lay more with service industries, including financial services. In the present recession, service employment has suffered as much, or even more than manufacturing.

Some day, perhaps, politicians will discover that they need all three of these remedies: an adequate and planned supply of skills; measures to reduce restrictive practices in industry and services; and a national consensus that covers not just incomes, but other factors in employees' living standards. British politics has a fatal addiction to either-or solutions.

Margaret Thatcher's long tenure at Downing Street has been the most remarkable in peacetime this century. In part, this was because it *was* so long, and that, in turn, was because of the dire and divided state of the Opposition. After James Callaghan retired, Labour descended into a long night of the soul. The party rejected a man many regarded as the best leader it never had, Denis Healey, and elected Michael Foot, in the hope of maintaining unity. But the Left was determined to push its long-frustrated hopes on policy and structure; and part of the Right, in the form of the Gang of Four, could take no more, and broke away to form the Social Democratic Party.

In the early 1980s, the Social Democrats joined David Steel's Liberals in an Alliance that aimed to 'break the mould' of British politics, either by replacing Labour as the principal alternative to the Conservatives or, through proportional representation, by making future British governments more likely to be coalitions than not. For a brief spell, the Alliance rode high, on one occasion reaching 50 per cent in the opinion polls, with Labour and Conservatives sharing the rest equally. But in the end, the Centre could not hold, and in 1983 the divisions among Mrs Thatcher's opponents made her re-election certain.

In the following Parliament, the Alliance, under the joint but divided leadership of the two Davids (Owen and Steel) was less effective. Neil Kinnock, as Labour's new leader, had begun to seize control of his party's machine, but was not yet ready to make the transformation in its policies that the voters seemed to require. So the 1987 election, in retrospect, was not all that difficult for Mrs Thatcher either.

Her early years had been difficult. She, too, was determined to break the mould. In her case, the aim was not constitutional reform, but to reverse the direction of post-war economic policy. It was a revolution for which her first Cabinet was not prepared. They had heard the rhetoric, but did not believe she could be serious. She was. As unemployment rose above three million for the first time since before the war, the One Nation wing of Toryism — whom Margaret Thatcher stigmatized as 'Wets' — was horrified. It was the memory of the Thirties that had turned Churchill from office in 1945, and caused the last great revolution in the Conservative Party's outlook.

When unemployment and racial tensions produced riots in many places, and Britain looked at risk from suffering 'long, hot summers' similar to those in America in the Sixties, many Tories thought election defeat, or worse, was coming. But a combination of Opposition disarray, victory over Arthur Scargill and the miners at home, and victory over the Argentines in the Falklands, assured Mrs Thatcher of victory. Meanwhile, she had assiduously weeded out the 'Wets' from the Cabinet, until by the middle of the decade she seemed to have a government very much in her own image.

Life, however, is never as simple as that. Her bitter quarrel with Michael Heseltine over the Westland helicopter affair — a harbinger of other European quarrels to come — put her office at risk. Margaret Thatcher had a mission on Europe. So long as she was attempting to reform the Community's budget, to win a better financial deal for Britain, to transform the Common Agricultural Policy, her party remained, by and large, behind her.

But during her third term, the Bruges Speech signalled more profound doubts about the 'ever closer union' to which Europe was now dedicated. The British Prime Minister seemed to be advocating the *Europe des Patries* that President De Gaulle had espoused a generation before. Europe had passed on from that, as had many MPs at Westminster, including significant members of Mrs Thatcher's Cabinet.

Several years before her fatal disputes with Nigel Lawson and Geoffrey

Howe over British membership of the Exchange Rate Mechanism, one of Toryism's most profound thinkers had warned me that the European issue could divide his party more than any subject since the repeal of the Corn Laws in the last century. In the event, it did more than anything else to drive her, reluctantly, from office.

Except, perhaps, the Community Charge, aka the Poll Tax. Margaret Thatcher's political stock-in-trade has been determination. The Russians, in Colder War days, dubbed her the Iron Lady. She embraced the image and gloried in her indomitable will, which she put at the service of her clear ideology. *Hubris* decreed that this determination should be the cause of her downfall.

For more than 15 years, long before she reached Downing Street, she had been determined to get rid of the rates as a means of financing local government. She prodded successive Environment Secretaries to produce an alternative. In the end, Kenneth Baker disobligingly obliged her. Nicholas Ridley led her deeper into the mire. Chris Patten was belatedly invited to rescue the Government from its crisis. Michael Heseltine, judging that a change was needed at the top, made the challenge, but did not inherit the crown, only the problem.

And so John Major, Neil Kinnock and Paddy Ashdown march on, targets for Les Gibbard's pen in the Nineties.

LIFE BEFORE THATCHER

'Pussy-cat, pussy-cat, where have you been?'   *19 May 1970*

Encouraged by a seven per cent polls lead, trusting in the support of newly enfranchised eighteen-year-olds and hoping well-heeled Tories would be holidaying, Harold Wilson called a June election.

Barbara Castle's 'In Place of Strife' proposal to curb unofficial strikes by using the law split Labour. In due course Wilson jettisoned it and unpopular pay controls as the 'Labour's Got Soul' campaign warmed up for the election.

16 June 1970

**'Here is Edward Bear, coming downstairs now, bump, bump, bump
on the back of his head . . .**

Ted Heath's hands were full countering Enoch Powell's outbursts on the 'enemy within', black immigration, and the evils of Europe. At no time did opinion polls place the Tories in front.

17

Fleet Street was united in predicting a Labour victory — so no cartoon of a Wilson defeat was drawn. The first results were relayed to thirsty *Guardian* journos 'resting' at the Blue Lion. Deputy features editor, David McKie, went pale, muttered that things were serious, and departed. At 11.15 Gibbard beheaded Harold and glued Ted Heath onto a cartoon with fortuitous imagery.

19 June 1970

10 July 1970

Ted Heath's first big challenge was a national dock strike in favour of a £20-a-week basic wage. The nation braced itself for food shortages and export losses as the troops moved in.

6 October 1970

There were more strikes in Heath's first year than in the year of the General Strike. While the public were urged to force workers back by condemnation, Robert Carr unveiled the Industrial Relations Bill fo fine 'wildcat' strikers.

Barbermedes Principle *22 January 1971*

As workers sought bigger slices of the cake, production costs rose, and as inflation soared so did unemployment as the workforce priced itself out of jobs.

25 February 1971

24 February 1971

A Concise History of British Immigration

Reggie Maudling's immigration bill halted the right of Commonwealth workers to settle in Britain unless they were patrial and with British parents or grandparents, thus ruling out most blacks and favouring the old Dominions. Nevertheless the *Guardian*'s cartoonist would have been sent packing but for marriage to a British passport-holder.

20 July 1971

Anthony Barber created a boom with his spend, spend, spend mini-budget abolishing all hire-purchase controls. The unemployed could only stand and watch.

21 January 1972

'Touched though I am, chaps, I regret I just cannot accept any more awards . . .

Unemployment reached the horrifying level of one million. Heath had won the Admiral's Cup in *Morning Cloud* in August and was recipient of awards for being a good European.

22 July 1972

**'We've arrested the ring-leaders, m'lud — in fact
we've arrested everything!'**

The Industrial Relations Act created more problems than solutions. The heavy hand of
the law arrested four London dockers as leaders of an unofficial strike. Despite the inver-
vention of the shadowy Official Solicitor to release the martyrs, a nationwide dock-strike
followed.

Hannibal Heath   *10 January 1973*

When TUC−CBI talks on voluntary wage and price restraint stalemated, the Government
imposed a compulsory pay and price freeze, breaking election pledges to shun an incomes
policy. There was union opposition.

15 February 1973

'Look, Feather, I don't care if you think it's a silly design — your place is underneath!'

Heath followed up the freeze with a second instalment. The TUC, who were used to more fraternal relationships with No.10, objected.

'Nice one, Tony — now keep it there!

17 May 1973

All the Fun of the Fair   *25 May 1973*

After photos of frolics with prostitutes were hawked around Fleet Street a Defence Minister, Lord Lambton, and the Tory leader in the Lords, Earl Jellicoe, resigned, reviving memories of the Profumo affair.

7 August 1973

Barber adopted a *laissez-faire* attitude while world commodity prices rocketed, adding to the cost of imports because of the fall in the value of the floating pound. A four per cent increase in interest rates added to the fun.

25

6 November 1973

In October Israel launched the Yom Kippur offensive, capturing an area from Sinai to the Suez Canal. The oil sheikhs quadrupled oil prices in an Arab backlash.

14 December 1973

To conserve electricity Britain began to work a three-day week. Miners banned overtime to break Phase 3 pay limits, leaving power stations with only forty per cent of their usual coal in the midst of an oil crisis.

18 January 1974

'Of course it's shrunk — I forgot to tell you it wasn't designed for floating!'

The pound had been floating since 1972 and had become very itsy bitsy teeny weeny, with inflationary effects on the cost of imports.

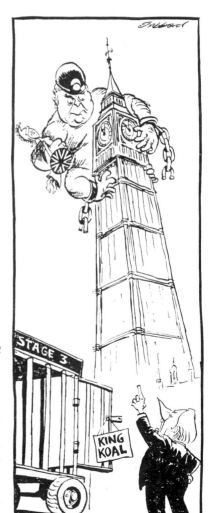

7 February 1974

'Just you come down this instant — or I'll ask the electorate who owns the building!'

There was now a full miners' strike. This cartoon appeared on the morning of Heath's decision to hold a 'Who Rules Britain?' election. One week before the vote the Pay Board announced that the Government figures on which miners' pay rates were calculated had been faulty — miners were actually eight per cent poorer than workers with whom they had been likened.

27

2 March 1974

The election left Harold Wilson with the most seats, but not an overall majority. Heath, four seats behind Wilson, would not budge from Downing Street while he wooed Liberal support. He failed and on 6 March Wilson became Prime Minister and ended the miners' strike by conceding most demands. In a second election on 11 October Wilson secured his overall majority by the finest margin of three seats.

15 October 1974

22 October 1974

Having lost twice, Ted Heath was urged by the 1922 Committee to do the decent thing, which he ignored. His main opponent, Sir Keith Joseph, knocked himself out of the Tory leadership contest with a peculiar speech which seemed to suggest that the poorer classes were unsuitable to have children and should desist. His philosophical torch was passed on to Margaret Thatcher.

In December Lord Home's Procedure Review Committee ruled that there should be facilities for annual elections of a Tory Leader.

4 February 1975

In a contest between Heath, Thatcher and Hugh Fraser, Margaret Thatcher won by 130 votes to Heath's 119. Heath immediately resigned.

29

'Well, I trust those voices she hears are the voters!'

Thatcher had secured grass-roots support and was too far ahead to be stopped in the second ballot by the likes of Jim Prior, Geoffrey Howe or John Peyton — or by the man who probably would have won had he stood in the first ballot, William Whitelaw. (Margaret Thatcher did indeed hear the voices of the punters, and in this drawing of her in Joan of Arc armour Les Gibbard lays claim to being the first person to portray her as an 'Iron Lady'!)

'But first all passengers will vote on whether we step ashore or continue our luxury cruise.'

Wilson had pledged a referendum on continuing membership of the EEC and some renegotiation of the terms of entry. (The Government, but not its party, had performed a U-turn from anti- to pro-EEC.) The referendum idea had been Tony Benn's and now he, Michael Foot and Peter Shore who had all campaigned against Europe found the popular vote being used to put a final end to their debate. They were defeated by 67.2 per cent to 32.8 per cent. It meant the end of pro-European Roy Jenkins's hopes of leading the party.

15 April 1975

In spite of the Social Contract with the unions, by which they volunteered to curb and monitor pay increases, wages had gone up 30 per cent in the past year and prices by 18 per cent. Rampant inflation dictated Denis Healey's budget, in which he cut public spending.

'Well, I did warn you about over-eating'

20 May 1975

'Young Jones here has made the awfully good suggestion that our parade would look better if everybody, regardless of size, covered the same ground with each pace!'

The transport union's leader Jack Jones, considered by some the most powerful man in the country, was dismayed by the excesses of the Social Contract and the triumph of those with muscle while the weak were left behind as settlements threatened to reach 40 per cent. His suggestion was a flat increase of £6 for everybody earning less than £8500.

'Perhaps we should pull the cord!'

The pound had lost a quarter of its 1971 value and inflation was approaching 22 per cent. Unions and management agreed that the situation was crazy, but nobody wanted to be left behind.

In June the pound nose-dived again, losing five cents in one day. With inflation running at 26 per cent the Jones £6 scheme was imposed by the Government with TUC support but much grass-root grumbling.

Discovering the Loss World   *31 July 1975*

Having to pay impossible wages, the nationalized industries made spectacular losses in spite of huge increases in domestic charges, such as 33 per cent for electricity.

8 April 1976

Harold Wilson had caused astonishment by resigning on 16 March. Jim Callaghan was beaten by Michael Foot in the first ballot then finally defeated him by 176 votes to 137 to become leader on 5 April.

Healey wanted to shift resources to manufacturing industry and pinned his faith on a second round of incomes policy. Inflation began to fall to 18.9 per cent.

27 April 1976

Agenda: Who Stands on Whose Shoulders to Get the Baler?

Sterling was considered by the Bank of England to be overvalued, but by signalling this the market went crazy with speculators selling down through the $2 mark to nearly $1.70. In June the Government borrowed £45.3 billion in standby credit for six months.

While Healey tried to withstand pressure from overseas creditors to cut public spending and put his economic house in order, party activists vocally pursued their dreams and election promises.

23 July 1976

'And so, the princess and the entire kingdom fell into a deep sleep to await the day when the as yet unborn Prince Boom would come to awaken the princess with a kiss...

To regain the confidence of the markets and to smooth the path to the IMF for financial help, Healey cut public spending by £1 billion and added a 2 per cent surcharge on employers' National Insurance contributions.

Tin Pan Allies   *9 September 1976*

The party of full employment was now indistinguishable from the Tories as the jobless total rose to 1.6 million by autumn 1977. (This cartoon was inspired by George Harrison's plagiarism case.)

21 September 1976

Callaghan warned a rebellious Labour Party conference that Britain had lived on borrowed time and could not spend its way out of a recession. The party reaction triggered more market panic and the pound plunged to $1.63, forcing Healey, waiting to fly east from Heathrow, to divert to Blackpool for a heckled five-minute speech from the floor. He announced that he was applying for an IMF loan based on existing policies but 'it means things we do not like as well as things we do'. The high drama was placed in perspective by the wink he gave me as he left the microphone.

November 1976

Britain applied to the IMF for a £3 billion facility. A puppet of the chief paymaster, the U.S. Treasury, it initially demanded £5 billion in public spending cuts and there was a suspicion that it was encouraged in this by some British civil servants who wanted to teach their masters a lesson.

'Shove off — I'm not done for yet!'   *24 March 1977*

In by-elections Callaghan had been deprived of his overall majority and when he lost attempts to introduce devolution to Wales and Scotland Thatcher challenged with a vote of no confidence. Big Jim lived to fight another day by entering into a Lib-Lab pact with David Steel. He was able to blame his party for not delivering the Liberals' proportional representation, while telling his own side that the Libs were to blame for his not pursuing more extreme socialist policies.

29 March 1977

The nation braced itself for more punishment, but Healey actually cut income tax from 35p to 33p while asking unions to reduce their pay claims.

5 April 1977

The TUC could no longer guarantee delivery. Many unions, including the fire brigades, rebelled against the restrictions of Phase 2.

7 May 1977

Somehow Callaghan kept rolling on, disregarding losses in local and by-elections. Another cartoon — showing Callaghan gliding through life on a banana skin and provoking a furious Thatcher response that if he was a gentleman he'd fall off — was secured by his daughter to give to the Prime Minister.

29 June 1977

'Look here — I'm not going in there unless the entire crew accepts me as co-pilot!'

Not content with taking all the flak for keeping Labour in power, the Liberals demanded more say in policy. Ministers had to clear actions with their Liberal counterparts before going to Cabinet. (The bombs being loaded signify some of the demands already met.) In July the Social Contract died and the TUC refused to set any levels for pay settlements.

27 October 1977

Two years earlier, Britain's last chance, North Sea oil, began to flow through the pipelines to land. The Government could now start to capitalize and Healey injected £1 billion into the economy in his mini-budget, much to the ire of Thatcher (who would preside over the best years of oil production).

24 November 1977

'I quite agree, it's a rough ride — but it might get us to the garage!'

With a troublesome Left-controlled national executive and uneasy relations with the Liberals, it was a bumpy ride for Callaghan and his deputy, Michael Foot.

David and Jimlieth

In April 1978, David Steel announced that Liberal support would end with the current Parliament. In the next decade he was to be known as the Boy David.

In 1978 Gibbard took a breather, animated full time, then left for New Zealand. In Britain Callaghan played cat and mouse with election dates, disappointed his allies' expectations by not going for an October poll, and was engulfed as the 5 per cent pay limit he demanded was swept aside by Ford with a 15 per cent settlement and the wage-claims dam burst.

The 'Winter of Discontent' which followed featured road-haulage, docks and public-employees strikes, alienating sympathy with images of unburied dead, uncollected rubbish and ungritted winter roads. The Tories were 20 per cent ahead in the polls although their leader lagged far behind Callaghan in popularity.

Devolution bills were passed but referenda in Wales rejected self-rule and the Scottish vote was too lukewarm to clinch a deal, so Scottish Nationalists withdrew their support from Labour.

On 28 March Labour lost a no-confidence motion by one vote and for the first time in 50 years a Government fell by a single vote in the Commons. It was the end of an era and Gibbard returned for the election.

ENTER MAGGIE :
The First Term

30 March 1979

'Drat! There doesn't seem to be one for making them give up without a fight!'

Callaghan wasn't giving up without a fight, and still commanded considerable popularity with the voters. He alleged that a Tory government would lead to increased unemployment, higher VAT and bankrupt companies. Cutting unions down to size and controlling inflation were her major cards, along with more law-and-order regulations and stronger defence measures.

The Tories won by 43 votes, in spite of Mrs Thatcher's poor showing in leadership polls. Gentlemanly as ever, the *Guardian* would not print this cartoon as Britain's first lady Prime Minister took office. Events have, however, shown that the cartoon was correct in indicating that this was no feminist revolution. No other woman rose to the top ranks of the Cabinet under Mrs T., and her emphasis on 'Family Values' indicated just where she thought women should stay.

7 May 1979

'Oh, don't worry about me — I'll just potter around in the background!'

There was no place for Ted Heath in Thatcher's Cabinet where he might spearhead 'Wet' opposition to her policies. Heath disdained offers of ambassadorships and settled down to what seemed to some to be a long sulk on the front row of the back benches.

43

12 June 1979

'And now, undaunted by all adversity, our Geoffrey will build a temple to capitalism without resorting to an ounce of taxpayers' mortar.'

There may have been less opportune times to launch an experiment, but an oil crisis triggered by the fall of the Shah of Iran took some beating. The cost of oil affected the Retail Prices Index and pushed wages up all over again.

13 June 1979

Freedom

Fulfilling the pledge to give people freedom to choose how to spend their money, Geoffrey Howe cut income tax by 3 per cent to 30 per cent and reduced the top rate by 23p in the pound. Though the Tories had denied they would raise VAT, the income-tax cuts were financed by a leap in Value Added Tax from 8 per cent to 15 per cent. Prices immediately soared and inflation rose 11.6 per cent in Thatcher's first year.

44

23 July 1979

With ideological fervour, Sir Keith Joseph at the Department of Industry started to sell off nationalized industry assets. Outright privatization was still considered a little bold, but the philosophy 'Private good, public bad' would guide future policy.

11 February 1979

'And about time too! Now look here — are you sure he'll rip out the jugular of anyone who crosses our path?'

The steel industry was in the grip of a seven-week-old strike against South Wales closures and monetarist zealots were convinced that mild-mannered Jim Prior was the wrong man to tame the unions. He produced relatively unprovocative proposals to control secondary picketing, finance union ballots and compensate victims of closed shops, and was constantly stabbed in the back by his leader who wanted the right to seize union funds.

Oh, What a Lovely Monetary Policy!   *28 August 1980*

Unemployment passed two million with the largest annual rise since 1930, and to add to the humiliation the American economy was being coaxed out of recession using the opposite policies.

30 August 1980

15 September 1980

'So I don't feed 'em enough? That shows what little you know about driving a team, mister! They've got each other to eat!'

While Thatcher maintained that her monetarist policies were absolutely right there were 40,000 redundancies a month as manufacturers reported falls in orders of 40 per cent.

15 October 1980

Trade-union leaders, such regular visitors to beer-and-sandwich occasions at Downing Street in the recent past, were now completely ignored.

'Bah, humbug — and while you're here, may I point out what a lousy mess you left behind you!'

The ghost of paternal Conservatism past protested from time to time but to no avail.

'Go and get another few thousand virgin school-leavers? Maybe sacrificing one middle-aged female of high rank would produce better results!'

With the ultimate tragedy of school-leavers going straight to the dole queue the Wets began to mutter among themselves but were basically too gutless to wish to appear disloyal.

Mrs Thatcher's Market Forces *13 July 1981*

The inner cities erupted with rioting in Toxteth in Liverpool, then London, Birmingham and other deprived centres. After further violence in Brixton, Michael Heseltine went to Liverpool to investigate the causes. While he favoured more investment Mrs T. tended towards more prison sentences.

14 July 1981

17 July 1981

'I hear some of you don't like our policy of torpedoing our own ships — well, here's your chance to step ten paces forward and show us how wet your position is!'

Cabinet critics of the monetary policy which had laid waste the economy were invited to have their say, but it was plain to them that Wets were viewed with contempt and there was no turning back.

9 October 1981

'By Jove, some chaps have no manners at all — leaving before the lady has finished her song!'

TINA (There Is No Alternative) and 'the lady's not for turning' became Thatcher catch-cries. Ted Heath, Geoffrey Rippon and fourteen heretics begged to differ, to the fury of the grassroots party.

'And so, Ted, the platform is yours'.   *14 October 1981*

Exorcism at Tory Towers

5 October 1981

4 December 1981

'Look, champ, I know what I'm doing. In a few years' time he'll slow down and take a nap — then we pounce!'

As Mrs T. blithely ploughed on, unemployment rose above three million for the first time since the 1930s. Wets and employers urged the Chancellor to invest in jobs.

6 February 1982

Freddie Laker's airline, the epitome of free enterprise — crashed, hit by the recession, exchange rates and the cost of borrowing.

Call of the Wild

1 March 1982

5 April 1983

The Ministry of Defence had decided to order the multi-warhead Trident to replace out-dated Polaris submarine nuclear defence, while also endorsing a NATO decision to base Cruise missiles in Britain. As a result there was an enormous resurgence in CND member-ship, and women camped permanently outside Greenham Common, the American-con-trolled base selected for the missiles.

10 May 1983

The election campaign had unofficially commenced in January with Mrs Thatcher's surprise visit to the Falklands to capitalize on Her Victory. Now she went for a June election, despite the fact that unemployment had just reached three million.

'Conclusive' Start   *16 May 1983*

Mrs Thatcher ended the election as she had started, in front. Michael Foot, chosen to heal Labour rifts, did not score with voters, while Roy Jenkins and David Steel made uneasy running-mates in the centre.

4 June 1983

'Here's your big chance — now I've got their attention you convert 'em!'

Denis Healey disturbed a hornets' nest by accusing Thatcher of capitalizing on the spilt blood of British soldiers.

9 June 1983

The day of choice. Mrs Thatcher favoured the death sentence, the centre hoped for a close result so that they could control the future, while Labour hoped its support would not drain away to the third parties. In fact many Labour voters gave Thatcher a vote to 'finish the job'.

THE FALKLANDS WAR

A D'Oyly Carte Farewell *21 February 1982*

The Government, needing money for the horrendously expensive Trident nuclear deterrent, cut costs in defence and signalled a lack of interest in the Falklands by withdrawing the supply ship *Endurance*. The aircraft-carrier *Invincible* was sold to the Australians as the real home of Gilbert and Sullivan, the D'Oyly Carte company, ran out of money and closed.

3 April 1982

The apparent willingness of the British to offload a troublesome South Atlantic responsibility encouraged Argentina to help themselves. South Georgia was taken over by scrap-metal merchants and Port Stanley invaded militarily. Britain discovered that its navy had been moth-balled or sold off, although Australia kindly lent back *Invincible*.

6 April 1982

Thatcher loathed the Foreign Office, and Lord Carrington and his team did the decent thing and resigned for not foreseeing the invasion. John Knott, who had presided over Britain's inadequate defences, soldiered on.

17 April 1982

In a galling exercise Thatcher had to take on arch-'Wet' Francis Pym to restore diplomatic credibility. But, from the moment a jingoistic special Saturday sitting of Parliament handed her the taskforce sword, no peace negotiations would stop her teaching the Argentinians a lesson.

10 April 1982

The jingoism was not at first reflected in the general public as the gun-boat force set off to prise the invaders off. Then loyalty to 'our lads', much encouraged by the right-wing tabloids, took over.

Tempus Fugit   *15 April 1982*

American Secretary of State, Al Haig, burnt up the air miles trying to prevent conflict with its knock-on effect on Latin American relations.

Sail and Steam   *15 April 1982*

'Never mind how you get a ship in a bottle –   *19 April 1982*
how do you get it out again?'

Special Boat Squadron men landed on South Georgia and prepared for a marines attack.

27 April 1982

'There's only room for us up here — but take my word for it, we're on course for our picnic at Negotiation Island and it's a lovely day!'

It was now Thatcher's war and the troublesome and less than 'patriotic' Opposition was excluded. South Georgia was recaptured and Thatcher commanded Britain to 'Rejoice!'

26 April 1982

Increasingly Parliament realized that it was impotent.

30 April 1982

'Huh! Appeasers! What on earth is the point of bringing along a battering ram if you don't use it!'

Labour favoured delay to allow negotiations to take off. The Government feared that its fleet would be sitting ducks for submarine or air attack.

The Price of Sovereignty Has Increased — Official. *6 May 1982*

The romantic vision of war was shattered when the Argentinian cruiser *General Belgrano* was sunk by the British submarine *Conqueror* and 362 men were killed. This also killed a most hopeful Peruvian peace plan. Before emotions could recover an Exocet missile sank the *Sheffield*.

I turned to the famous cartoon by Philip Zec, which nearly had the *Daily Mirror* closed down during the Second World War. The cartoon of a merchant seaman clinging to ocean debris was entitled 'The price of petrol has been increased by one penny — Official'. It was intended to portray the terrible price paid in lives for the nation's petrol and the immorality of waste, but was interpreted as an attack on profiteering oil companies and was hotly debated in Parliament.

The day after publication of my version I returned home to phone calls asking if I had seen the *Sun*'s leader, and what did I think of being called a traitor along with BBC TV's Peter Snow. It seemed ironical that I should be accused of treason by a newspaper whose owner changed nationality whenever it suited him to acquire more newspapers and television stations, but I held my tongue.

However, there was an unsought-for thunder of hooves and the National Union of Journalists galloped 'to the rescue', ousting the *Sun*'s leader-writer for unfraternal and unprofessional conduct. In truth, Peter Snow and I were caught in the cross-fire between two battling tabloid giants — the pro-war *Sun* and anti-war *Mirror*.

Bernard Levin rang to check that I was taking no legal action then devoted his *Times* column to an attack on do-gooders creating a full-scale battle out of something Messrs Snow and Gibbard were sensible and honourable enough to ignore.

Thatcher appeared to consider that the Opposition had excluded itself from any say in the war and carried on untethered.

'Our proposals are no longer on the table — Mrs T.'   *21 May 1982*

British troops established a beachhead at San Carlos Bay.

31 May 1982

The suffering of men was a small price for arms buyers, dealers and manufacturers the world over, who eagerly studied the performance and failings of the latest technology in action.

22 May 1982

2 June 1982

In a two-pronged attack, British troops fought their way across rugged terrain to knock at Port Stanley's back door.

67

Back to the Wall   *4 June 1982*

'Ssshhh, from you-know-where.'   *14 June 1982*

All bad news was censored by the military, but not everything had turned out smiles, particularly at the bloody Bluff Cove conflict. The Argentinians eventually surrendered at Port Stanley and the war ended with 255 British casualties and 652 Argentinians dead.

16 June 1982

While Thatcher celebrated, Argentina fumed. Galtieri was ousted and later arrested when a civilian government replaced the military junta. Not particularly magnanimous in victory, Thatcher would not talk to Argentina for years.

19 January 1983

The Franks Report absolved Thatcher and the Cabinet of any blame for the invasion of the Falklands. As it also ruled that the invasion could not have been foreseen or prevented, Carrington & Co's sacrifice and the pillorying of the FO seemed uncalled for.

22 April 1983

The Prime Minister made a surprise visit to the Falklands in January to enjoy the fruits of her victory. She then violently opposed the wish of Argentinian parents to visit the graves of their conscript sons as 'propaganda'.

13 June 1983

As predicted in 7 April's cartoon, Francis Pym was eaten alive once the Falklands victory assured Thatcher of a landslide election victory.

8 November 1983

Defence Minister Michael Heseltine made a decision to mislead the public and resist persistent questioning into the truth of the *Belgrano* sinking. Top civil servant Clive Ponting was disgusted and sent incriminating papers to the relentless questioner, Labour's Tam Dalyell.

Ponting was prosecuted under the Official Secrets Act. His plea that public duty was more important than obedience to a minister won over a jury and he was acquitted.

14 February 1985

... But the real truth never surfaced.

RETURN OF THE IRON LADY
... and the Westland Affair

10 June
1983

'You are to be congratulated on ignoring all those scare stories about being trapped in an emergency — my, doesn't it cut out that disagreeable noise outside!'

The Tories were back with a landslide victory and a parliamentary majority of 144. Labour was wiped out in the south and the Liberal-Social Democrat alliance, despite 25 per cent of the vote, made no great advances in seats. The Tories in fact scored fewer votes than they had in 1979, a fact lost in the 'landslide' euphoria.

4 October 1983

'It's not the men in my life, it's the life in my men that counts' — Mae West

Within three days of the election Roy Jenkins bowed out as SDP leader and Michael Foot also resigned. Dr David Owen, the ambitious former Labour Foreign Secretary now led the SDP while an overwhelming majority of Labour's electoral college selected the left-winger Neil Kinnock as their new leader. Mrs T. was coming up to her 58th birthday.

15 October 1983

The 'victory' Tory party conference was marred by revelations 'putting the record straight' by Sara Keays, former secretary of Party Chairman Cecil Parkinson, who had reneged on a promise to marry her although she was carrying his child. Reluctantly Parkinson resigned, although Mrs T. tried to save him.

26 October 1983

To show that the US would not tolerate Marxism in its 'back-yard' the Marines invaded the tiny Caribbean country of Grenada. Britain, and Grenada's Head of State, the Queen, were kept in the dark.

A Special Relationship *27 October 1983*

Thatcher raged at Reagan on the telephone, but increasingly it appeared that Britain was paying the price of being beholden for US assistance during the Falklands campaign.

22 May 1984

Jim Prior, a former industrialist and Tory 'Wet' who had been excluded from economic decisions by being reshuffled against his will to Northern Ireland in 1981, was visibly unhappy at the direction being taken by the monetarist mafia. He resigned in September 1984.

'Whoops! Missed!' *12 June 1984*

The Labour-dominated Greater London Council with its spartan-living leader, Ken Livingstone, and its banners announcing the latest London jobless total from the opposite side of the river to Parliament made Mrs T. see red. She set out to abolish the GLC (originally a Tory creation) and even a rearguard action by the Lords came to nought.

4 October 1984

Throughout Europe the Ban the Bomb movement had achieved massive dimensions and British anxieties were fuelled by a television film, *The Morning After,* depicting the horrors of the nuclear winter after a nuclear war. Most people were more scared by Michael Heseltine's appearance on TV immediately after the film — 'in the interests of balance'.

29 January 1985

In spite of 3.25 million sacrificed unemployed and the promise of tax cuts, the great god Market Forces was not satisfied; there was wild activity on the Stock Exchange and the pound fell to a lowest ever near-parity with the dollar.

19 March 1985

'And with one bound. . .'   *24 July 1985*

In spite of Tory back-bench and grass-roots constituency opposition, Thatcher steam-rolled through high pay-increases for judges, generals and top civil servants.

WESTLAND

8 January 1986

Westland, Britain's only helicopter manufacturer, was in financial trouble and sought Government help. State aid was frowned on and the company was recommended to seek a take-over. Mrs Thatcher favoured an American one, Defence Secretary Michael Heseltine not only favoured, but single-handedly created, a European offer.

The Westland directors were peeved, as they wanted the US offer, but Heseltine darkly threatened loss of European defence contracts if they fell into the clutches of the Americans.

10 January 1986

A ministerial board had been appointed to look at the latest Euro offers before the deadline expired but it was never convened and Thatcher denied knowledge of it. However, Heseltine continued his campaign, to the irritation of the recently appointed Trade Secretary, Leon Brittan, and the Prime Minister herself, who dithered about sacking Heseltine. Instead she requested the Solicitor-General's opinion of Heseltine's warnings on Euro contracts, and recommended that he should write to the Defence Secretary, pointing out his worries about material inaccuracies. Copies of the letter were sent to Downing Street and the Department of Trade and Industry, whose press office, after consultation with their No.10 counterparts (who concurred but wanted clean hands), leaked its contents to the Press Association. The Solicitor-General was furious.

Three days later the Cabinet met and an outraged Heseltine stormed out when Thatcher insisted that all further statements on Westland should be cleared by Downing Street.

15 January 1986

The Opposition could not believe their luck as Heseltine condemned Thatcher's dictatorial ways and the breakdown of Cabinet government. Meanwhile the Attorney-General threatened a police investigation into the leak, which had violated the sanctity of a law officer's correspondence.

Batting for Brittan   *24 January 1986*

At first Mrs Thatcher evaded facing the Commons, and left it to Trade and Industry Secretary Leon Brittan to carry the can for a leak from his department. However, in trying to avoid a difficult question from Heseltine he misled the House and had to return in the evening to apologize.

Mrs Thatcher eventually faced MPs and admitted involvement of her officials but personal ignorance of the leak. Tory back-benchers were baying for blood and under relentless pressure Brittan resigned — and was given a never-to-be-honoured pledge of early return to high office.

The Near-sighted Maggieoo *27 January 1986*

Mrs Thatcher spent an uncomfortable weekend making light of the crisis on television, but secretly worried that the next day's censure debate might be her last as Prime Minister.

28 January 1986

With a lacklustre performance from Neil Kinnock and a few calming words from Heseltine the issue lost steam. But, badly dented by Westland and the secrecy surrounding the sinking of the *Belgrano*, Thatcher's reputation for honesty had been irreparably damaged.

14 February 1986

As part of the post-Westland backlash the Government dropped plans to sell Austin-Rover to Ford. The Cabinet found new boldness to distance themselves from the PM and create their own collective responsibility.

31 March 1986

London's democratically elected Labour government was finally executed by a Tory majority in both houses at Westminster.

15 April 1986

Ronald Reagan, who had been itching to bloody Libya's nose for payrolling international terrorism, seized on a Berlin bombing as an excuse to plan an aerial attack. Thatcher agreed to the use of F-111s based on British soil and pressured Europe to support the US. Neither the Cabinet nor the country were pleased with her decision.

A Tale of Two Airstrips *25 April 1986*

Reagan and Thatcher berated Europe for not supporting the bloody venture. Europe instead braced itself for terrorist reprisal and, not for the last time, American tourists all stayed at home for fear of getting hurt. (Libya was actually innocent of the Berlin bomb.)

25 July 1986

The twin spectres of Westland and the *Belgrano* sinking would not go away.

19 December 1986

Continuing her 'American is Best' crusade, Thatcher dealt a final blow to a British long-range surveillance aircraft (headed by former 'Wet' Cabinet colleague, Jim Prior) by backing Boeing.

12 February 1987

To ensure the success of privatization, shares in nationalized industries were offered at knock-down prices. The Government simply shrugged off the huge profits made as shareholders immediately sold them on the open market.

31 March 1987

'Charming little place you have here — but all these ghastly furnishings will have to go!'

Thatcher laid claim to discovering that the pre-leadership Gorbachev was a man to do business with. Her visit to the USSR was soured by her outburst on Russian attitudes to civil liberties and their possible delay of disarmament talks.

9 May 1987

A split Opposition made a third Tory victory a dead cert, even if 60 per cent of the voters didn't want the Conservatives.

23 May 1987

Thatcher would not rethink her commitment to the multi-warheaded Trident, even though East-West relations were thawing. Labour came out worst in the defence virility stakes.

29 May 1987

'Heavens above! That we should've lived to witness a Presidential-style campaign in this country!'

Labour enlisted the music of Brahms and director Hugh Hudson (of *Chariots of Fire*) for a heart-welling political broadcast on behalf of the Kinnocks. Thatcher was perceived by the public as cold and uncaring, but Reagan liked her.

8 June 1987

World leaders met in Venice for an economic summit, providing many photo opportunities for a stateswoman. In the TV ice-cream commercial parodied here, an Italian on a bridge actually snatches the ice cream — but on 12 June the Tories romped home with 375 seats to Labour's 229 and the Alliance's 22.

BRING ME THE HEAD of ARTHUR SCARGILL!

19 February 1972

The miners had been quiet since 1926 but in September 1971, angry at the way they had fallen in the pay league, they claimed a 47 per cent increase and backed it with a 55.8 per cent vote for strike action.

In February they flexed their muscle at a Saltley gas works, where Yorkshire pickets led by the unknown Arthur Scargill spearheaded demonstrations building up to 15,000 people and succeeded in turning trucks away. As coke shortages mounted, lights went out and Whitehall panicked and paid the miners 20 per cent plus concessions as recommended by Lord Wilberforce.

24 October 1973

'Oh come, come, old chap — Phase 3 was just Ted's little joke!'

As Heath introduced Phase 3 of his incomes policy, strenuous attempts were made to defuse miners' and electricity workers' discontent with special threshold arrangements. The Yom Kippur war, with its effect on oil prices, surprised everyone and Heath confused the issue by extending thresholds to all, to cover any import price increases. The NUM, having lost special status, fumed and rejected 13 per cent, demanding 40 per cent and pointing to the quadrupling of oil prices and coal's new importance.

A Night at the Ballot — 'The Dying Swan'   *24 January 1974*

Heath rejected the suggestion that the miners were a special case and the NUM called an overtime ban, triggering a State of Emergency. A three-day week began in December and a TUC mediation offer for miners was rejected by Heath. The miners held a strike ballot.

5 February 1974

With 81 per cent of the miners in favour of a strike there seemed no choice but to hold a 'Who Rules' election, which Heath announced on 7 February.

22 February 1974

One week before the election the Pay Board reported that the miners were actually 8 per cent worse off than the Government had assumed in relationship to similar workers' wages, and the door was opened for increased pay under Phase 3. However, it was too late for Heath who, under attack for soaring shop prices and vulgar big-bank profits, managed four seats fewer than Labour and was ousted from Government.

The Pits and the Pendulum *20 February 1981*

Seven years later, the Conservatives were back in power under Margaret Thatcher. In response to Government pressure on borrowing, the Coal Board proposed closing twenty-three pits at the cost of 13,000 jobs. The miners threatened action, supported by steel, transport and seamen's unions. Thatcher judged the time was wrong to tame the miners and swiftly backed down.

2 March 1983

The Government built up huge coal reserves, encouraged power to diversify into oil and battle-hardened its police during the urban riots. The international glut of cheap oil was the signal for Norman Tebbit's 'On yer bike' statement which loomed over pits under threat of closure.

10 April 1984

'Actually I don't know what I think of all this — I'm just tagging along to make sure the horse doesn't get hurt!'

Arthur Scargill considered Thatcher's landslide victory with 31 per cent of the vote an undemocratic travesty and vowed to bring the Government down from outside. The PM selected as his opponent Ian MacGregor, a Scots American past retirement age who had been secured from Lazard Freres for a bargain £1.8 million to improve British Steel's fortunes. Scargill viewed Mrs T.'s hard man as a butcher out to destroy the industry.

Twice Scargill failed to move the membership to industrial action, but by deft use of union rules, he manoeuvred them into a strike without a ballot. Labour was concerned but found it hard to counter his more-socialist-than-thou attitude.

5 September 1984

With 25,000 Nottingham miners refusing to give their support without a ballot, the strike was fatally flawed. The courts ruled that Scargill's Yorkshire 'flying pickets' should stay in their own area, but this was not enforced. In May at Orgreave, police appeared in full riot gear for the first time and miners were charged several times by mounted police. Peace talks were angry occasions with no common ground.

17 October 1984

**'It appears they have enough snowballs to keep them going throughout the winter —
and will we go away!'**

The High Court had ruled that the strike was illegal in September. It now fined the union
£200,000 for contempt of court. Miners gained heart when the pit overseers' union
(NACODS) voted for strike action when management threatened that they would lose their
jobs if they did not cross NUM picket lines. The arbitration service, ACAS, made no progress in ending the dispute.

30 October 1984

The allegedly non-interventionist Government leaned on MacGregor to make peace with
NACODS and the strike threat was withdrawn. Scargill scored an own-goal with exposed
attempts to raise money from terrorism's paymaster, Gaddafi, while MacGregor ineptly
revealed Coal Board rifts by silencing his new troubleshooting PR man, Michael Eaton.

10 November 1984

A Dublin court froze NUM funds of £2.7 million but £6 million had already slipped out of the country to avoid sequestration to pay contempt-of-court fines. Scargill made full use of a free market liberated by the Tories. Faced with financial ruin, many miners drifted back to work.

31 January 1985

'On second thoughts, that's too easy — tell your lad to hold the apple in front of his heart!'

As the trickle of miners returning to work became a torrent, Scargill held out for unconditional negotiations, but the Government demanded unconditional surrender. Scargill had always insisted that there was a hidden programme of pit closures, which was sadly proved true later.

5 March 1985

With more than half the labour force back at work the strike ended. Scargill never officially surrendered, and refused to use his casting vote at an executive tied vote. The strike's legacy was an impotent and bankrupt union, excluded from industry decision-making while the breakaway Notts union thrived, and chaos within the Labour Party. The Government accelerated pit closures and by the Nineties the South Wales coalfield was almost non-existent.

13 October 1988

'Ups-a-daisy, old chap — the PM wants to bury someone else in there!'

Ever the vindictive victor, Thatcher, through her resurrected favourite, Cecil Parkinson, let it be known that coal would be privatized when feasible — a cruel conclusion to Scargill's socialist crusade.

100

GUNNING
FOR THE NHS

26 March 1971

It was the Heath government, and in particular Sir Keith Joseph whose philosophy would shape the emergent Thatcher, which determined that patients should pay more for prescriptions.

1 June 1983

The first Thatcher government gave immediate help to private medicine, increased prescription charges, insisted on contracting out non-medical services and provoked eight months of industrial action by COHSE unskilled workers. Documents leaked during the 1983 election campaign showed that the PM had even bolder ideas for dismantling the costly system and opening it up to market forces.

Cuckoo in the Nightingale Nest   *24 September 1983*

To the protests of doctors and nurses the NHS was compelled by Norman Fowler to seek private tenders for cleaning, catering and laundry, threatening the jobs of 250,000 ancillary workers.

103

1 October 1983

Fowler conceded that the Government's one per cent squeeze on the NHS budget would cost 5000 jobs.

Secrecy surrounded Tory deliberations on the future of the Welfare State, prompted by the realization that Britain would soon be top-heavy with white-haired citizens with very little young blood to finance their care. The Opposition felt, and were, excluded. Thatcher maintained that no details of winners or losers could emerge for two years.

Lady of the Lamp   *24 April 1987*

As the election loomed, Mrs Thatcher was widely perceived by the public as harsh, uncaring and lacking in compassion. Having previously refused to pay nurses the full amount awarded by an independent review body, the lady did a U-turn and paid in full.

5 June 1987

Thatcher's election pledges that the Health Service was safe in her hands were viewed with suspicion, since her own visits to hospital had all been private. After the election, monetarist zealot John Moore was put in charge of the NHS. Free dental check-ups and eye tests were to be abolished.

21 January 1988

The three presidents of the Colleges of Surgeons, Obstetricians and Physicians publicly deplored the cash-starvation of the NHS, demanding good-quality care for all and no two-tier system. Nurses at three London hospitals voted for a 24-hour stoppage, but Treasury Secretary John Major said there was no money.

3 February 1988

Angry nurses marched on Whitehall, providing only emergency cover in hospitals. The British Medical Association warned that the NHS was in terminal decline and demanded a £1.5 billion cash injection and guarantees of its continued existence as a service financed by the taxpayer. Thatcher tried to drive a wedge between the 'no-strike' Royal College of Nursing and other health unions, and set up a review to look at the NHS's future including increased private involvement.

22 April 1988

In his budget, Chancellor Nigel Lawson took advantage of a tax windfall from falling unemployment to throw away £4 billion in tax cuts mainly for the better-off. Top people also received additional pay awards.

Prescription charges had been raised 20p to £2.60, 100,000 people had marched for better funding of the NHS, and the Bishop of Durham called Tory policies 'wicked'. As local elections approached, Thatcher agreed to a pay rise of 18 per cent for the nurses, dependent on restructuring and grading.

1 February 1989

The luckless John Moore's empire was divided into two and Kenneth Clarke took over Health to steam-roller through Thatcher's wishes. Charges for dental and eye checks were almost defeated by a Tory back-bench revolt, but undeterred Clarke relentlessly sought ways to introduce market values.

15 December 1989

The next battlefield was with the enormously popular ambulance drivers in a dispute running from September to February. The ambulancemen wanted more than 6.5 per cent but Thatcher was not to be moved.

31 January 1989

With mass marches, public support remained remarkably high despite tragic deaths through the late response of police and army replacement vehicles. Ambulancemen maintained that they would answer emergency calls but were kept from doing so. The strike ended unsatisfactorily in February with a two-year 13 per cent deal described triumphantly as 'staggering' by the union but in reality it simply repackaged the original offer by Clarke.

7 June 1990

In spite of vigorous opposition from Labour, charges for eye tests became a fact of life.

ECONOMY OF TRUTH :
Gagging the BBC

The Spy Who Came in From the Cold   *17 July 1984*

In January, without warning, trade unions were banned from the Government Communications Headquarters at Cheltenham and employees offered £1000 compensation – your money or your job.

Civil-service strikes had lost GCHQ many working days and Thatcher was sensitive to US criticism of a leaky Secret Service. She rejected union pledges not to disrupt any more in exchange for union rights. The High Court ruled that her action was illegal.

23 November 1984

Unluckily for GCHQ workers, the Court of Appeal overruled the decision, and a later ruling stated that matters of national security were beyond the courts' jurisdiction. All remaining trade-unionists at GCHQ were sacked in September 1988.

7 March 1985

'Here it is in black and white — the invisible man assures us that the invisible watchdog is constantly on the statutory lead!'

Three former prime ministers rejected persistent suggestions of anti-Left bias in the Secret Service and of past attempts to destabilize Labour Governments.

1 August 1985

'What nonsense! I've got no influence here — why the controls are in his hands!'

Eager to please Thatcher, Home Secretary Leon Brittan attacked BBC plans to show the programme *Real Lives*, including an IRA terrorist interview. Brittan protested that it was the BBC governors' own decision, while muttering threats about introducing advertising on the state channel. The programme was withdrawn but shown two months later.

113

1 November 1986

'What a rotten, slanted picture — I insist you have your eyes tested!'

The BBC was a den of Marxists to most Tories. Party Chairman Norman Tebbit gunned down the messenger to distract from the message that the bombing of Libya was bloody and deeply unpopular. Reporter on the spot, Kate Adie, was vilified by Tebbit who promised a dossier of BBC bias and malpractice.

8 December 1986

To put the lid on the flood of Secret Service disclosures, Thatcher made an example of the memoirs of a discontented ex-MI5 officer, Peter Wright, now living in Tasmania. In July newspapers were banned from publishing any information derived from him.

The Cabinet Secretary, Sir Robert Armstrong, was humiliated in the Australian courts on Thatcher's behalf, having to apologize for misleading evidence and being 'economical with the truth'.

The book was published in America, but although the rest of the world could read it, and for a small fee locals could buy copies from entrepreneurs on British roadsides, Thatcher was determined to pursue the obligation of confidentiality through every court in the system. This also served to cover up Wright's revelations that a small band of MI5 men had tried to upset the Wilson Government.

3 February 1987

Special Branch raided BBC offices in Glasgow where investigative journalist and whistle-blower Duncan Campbell (the gargoyle) was preparing a programme on a secret spy satellite. Thatcher told an outraged Opposition that the seizure of two van loads of material, and threats of prosecution if the *New Statesman* published script extracts, were nothing to do with her.

28 April 1987

The contemptuous attitude towards democracy by MI5 plotters against Wilson was considered a lesser sin than contempt of court when details appeared in the press.

16 July 1987

'. . . and accordingly I rule that if one person's light is red, so is everybody else's.'

The *Guardian, Observer, Independent* and later the *Sunday Times* directly challenged the Government by publishing extracts from Wright's *Spycatcher*. The Government responded with injunctions, and a curious court-ruling that an injunction on one newspaper applied to all others tempted to follow.

31 July 1987

Thatcher was content to squander public funds, override press freedom and the public's right to know in a seemingly crazed mission to silence talkative public servants.

The March of Time

15 December 1987

My Country, Right or Wrong, a BBC radio programme on the Secret Service, was silenced by courts and Government pressure on BBC governors.

11 February 1988

As Thatcher pursued her vendetta against Wright to the highest courts of the land it was clear that judges did not agree that the obligation of confidentiality overruled public interest.

8 March 1988

Three known IRA activists were gunned down by undercover SAS men in Gibraltar where they had allegedly planted a car bomb. According to the Foreign Secretary they were challenged and went for their guns and a bomb had been found. With enthusiasm reminiscent of the despatch of the Falklands task-force Parliament warmly welcomed the news, although the news that there was in fact no bomb dampened enthusiasm.

Trials by Television   *29 April 1988*

A Loyalist gunman killed three and injured 50 at an IRA funeral in Belfast on 16 March. Three days later a mob beat up and shot dead two plain-clothed soldiers who drove by accident into a televised IRA cortege. Thatcher demanded that television channels should release all unused footage to identify the killers. Meanwhile, Howe tried to stop Thames TV showing *Death on the Rock*, which produced witnesses who claimed that no warning was given by the SAS in the Gibraltar slaughter.

30 June 1988

The Government scrapped the more ludicrous aspects of the Official Secrets Act. However, Secret Servicemen were now bound to eternal secrecy, and lost the defences of 'in the public interest' and 'prior publication'.

The Invisible Man Revealed   *23 November 1988*

Peter Wright triumphed and the House of Lords ruled that mention could be made of his book in the British press. Thatcher hinted at seizing the profits but anyone who had read the book wondered what all the fuss was about.

27 January 1989

'Since you're here, would you like to check the balance of this one?'

Death on the Rock, condemned by the Government as 'trial by television', was cleared by an independent inquiry. Thatcher rejected the findings.

3 February 1989

'To the rescue, chaps! Her lovely little hands must be in a terrible state from tying all those knots!'

Tory back-benchers abdicated responsibility to the public and submitted to their leader's crusade against leaks in the Civil Service, leaving the Opposition to fight forlornly.

Thatcher found herself in the strange position of supporting writers' freedom when the Ayatollah Khomeini decreed Salman Rushdie a blasphemer for his novel *The Satanic Verses* and ordered his execution.

An Outing With Grandpa

The unelected Upper Chamber put up a more spirited defence of the public's right to know than the Commons, and introduced many amendments.

1 February 1990

The Government was forced to admit to anti-IRA disinformation policy during the early 1970s, as alleged by former Ulster army press officer Colin Wallace, who also stated that there had been a dirty-tricks campaign to destabilize Harold Wilson's Government.

THIRD TIME
UNLUCKY
... featuring Poll Tax

13 June 1987

An impressively professional Labour campaign failed to stop Thatcher being the first Prime Minister ever to win three consecutive terms. The Tories won 375 seats to Labour's 229 and the Alliance's 22. The affluent and yuppie South was Tory and the neglected North-East Labour, prompting the PM to pledge something would 'have to be done' about inner cities. William Whitelaw, for a long time a stabilizing influence on Thatcher, retired from the Cabinet through ill-health.

15 June 1987

Court favourite, Cecil Parkinson, returned from his love-child exile while Westland human sacrifice, Leon Brittan, remained in the cold along with Heseltine. John Biffen paid the price for his 'semi-detached' independence in criticizing Thatcherism, while the last remaining Wet, Peter Walker, was exiled to Wales. Tebbit and Hailsham strode off into the sunset.

26 October 1987

'You know, I don't feel half so bad about not winning the big prize!'

On Black Monday, 19 October, the bottom fell out of the stock market after the Wall Street crash the previous Friday. The fools' paradise of ever-climbing share values unmatched by manufacturing output came crushing down.

The Return of the Cannon Fodder   *13 November 1987*

Unemployment fell significantly, providing the Government with a little good cheer, the bonus of a taxation windfall and un-Thatcherite thoughts of increased public spending.

10 February 1988

Thatcher voted against the experimental televising of Parliament, saying she feared the reputation of the House would suffer. Others suspected that she was scared of how her increasingly bellicose Question Time appearances would translate to the small screen. The Commons outvoted the PM and did the public — and political cartoonists — tremendous service.

26 February 1988

To justify privatizing the power industry, Cecil Parkinson was forced to create a grotesque structure of companies to merit the phrases 'competition' and 'market forces'.

126

Chancellor Nigel Lawson had engineered the Tory election victory by creating a pre-election boom. Now the trade deficit began to grow as a spendthrift public clamoured for imported luxuries. UK manufacturing meanwhile, remained starved of investment. Lawson was determined to cut taxes but fearful of the consequences.

16 March 1988

Lawson cut standard-rate income tax by 2p and the highest rate by 20 per cent, releasing £4 billion spending power onto the market. By restricting mortgage tax relief to one person per house he started a property stampede as groups and unmarried couples tried to beat the deadline and capitalize on the previous system.

Opinion polls suggested that most people thought tax cuts were less important than adequate spending on job creation, health and education, which were largely ignored in the budget.

18 March 1988

Thatcher tried to overrule Lawson's shadowing of the Deutschmark, fearing that such a link was an overture to joining the European Monetary System. But the economic miracle-worker persevered, lowering interest rates

18 May 1988

Bank rates fell to 7.5 per cent, the lowest in 10 years, but sterling continued to rise despite a bad trade deficit. Sir Geoffrey Howe joined forces with Lawson to force Thatcher to state that she was in full accord with her chancellor's financial policy.

16 June 1988

Gangs of English football hooligans terrorized German cities and fought riot police during the European championships. Thatcher decreed that something must be done.

29 June 1988

The Trickle-down Effect

Having cut taxes for the rich and triggered a spending boom, mainly on imports, Lawson faced a £1.2 billion deficit. Interest rates went up to 10 per cent as a form of control. The rich got richer and those in debt sank into deeper trouble.

4 November 1988

Kinnock had an impressive youthful group of Shadow Ministers working as a team; Thatcher mercilessly trampled over the hopes of colleagues by dismissing them as likely successors.

25 November 1988

Water, the most unlikely privatization, appeared in the Queen's Speech. The gift of nature was to become a gift to the French, who busily bought a controlling interest in the nation's essential asset.

6 December 1988

'Most of the egg production in this country sadly is now infected with salmonella,' said the upward-thrusting Junior Health Minister, Edwina Curry, who cost the nation £10 million in compensation to egg producers with her nearly true words which upset a powerful lobby and lost her her job.

17 January 1989

A computerized identity-card scheme to control football troublemakers was bulldozed through. Clubs feared closures and the loss of spectators.

18 January 1989

22 February 1989

British Muslims threatened violence as the Ayatollah ruled that Salman Rushdie should die for his published blasphemy. Europe and America showed remarkable unity in championing freedom of expression. Britain broke diplomatic relations with Iran and Rushdie went into hiding for a long, long time.

Enter the Green Goddess   *3 March 1989*

Thatcher suddenly discovered the environment. A trained scientist, she threw herself into initiatives to save the ozone layer and successfully motivated some other countries into action.

Lawson dashed hopes of increased Government spending with a tight budget notable only for reducing the price of unleaded petrol.

8 April 1989

Lord Chancellor Mackay's efforts to reform the legal profession and open up High Court advocacy to others outside the Bar ran into trouble. One hundred senior judges threatened strike action.

11 April 1989

The scheme which guaranteed dockers jobs for life was axed by the Government as a prelude to privatization. Under new Tory legislation, any protest strike would have been political and therefore illegal, as it was not a direct dispute with the employers.

28 April 1989

Ten years of Thatcher rule — Labour ungraciously pointed instead to the thousands of homeless now sleeping in the streets of the capital as a result of policies.

13 June 1989

**'I may lean in another direction —
but our course is identical!'**

Thatcher's favourite economic guru, Professor Alan Walters, was to return to Downing Street, letting reporters know that he thought the Chancellor's policies were misguided and cutting interest rates a mistake. Lawson no longer looked indispensable.

26 July 1989

'Changing the orchestra won't affect the tune — they're only there for appearances!'

Mrs T. didn't seem to need a cabinet. With pettiness and vindictiveness she reshuffled. Sir Geoffrey Howe, who had sided with Lawson in favour of the EMS, lost his beloved Foreign Office, to be replaced by inexperienced Treasury Secretary, John Major. Howe, now Leader of the House, was compensated with the deputy premiership — a job meaning nothing according to the Downing Street press office.

27 July 1989

Thatcher also alienated Douglas Hurd, the Home Secretary, whose job had been offered to Howe. She then stole Lawson's official country residence to compensate Howe for the loss of Chevening and thereby, brilliantly, earned the resentment of three senior ministers!

27 October 1989

As the Deutschmark rose, interest rates soared to 15 per cent, the highest for eight years, and mortgage-payers groaned under the pressure. Lawson considered that Britain should join Europe's Exchange Rate Mechanism as soon as possible. He confronted Thatcher, saying he could not longer tolerate the sniping of her adviser Walters — one of them would have to go.

At Question Time in the House, Thatcher shrugged off suggestions of trouble between her adviser and her Chancellor saying: 'Advisers advise; ministers decide.' An enraged Lawson stormed into Downing Street with his resignation. Thatcher could not comprehend a top minister resigning over such a thing, but worse came when Lawson told the Commons that she must appoint ministers she trusted then let them carry out policy — and rejected her version that she had done everything possible to stop his resignation. He urged Britain to join the EMS as soon as possible.

Walters also resigned in shock. Major, after the briefest of stays at the Foreign Office, moved back to the Treasury as Chancellor, and Hurd replaced him.

138

2 November 1989

Thatcher, chastened and contrite, undertook to consult the Cabinet more — but her autocratic instincts were irrepressible.

23 November 1989

Enter the Panto Stalking Horse (or Knightmeyer)

Hoping to encourage a heavyweight contender, Sir Anthony Meyer, a back-bencher, became Thatcher's first leadership challenger in 14 years. The favourites, not wishing to be branded disloyal, left him to it and he only won the support of sixty malcontents.

1 December 1989

'Oh, stop whining! It's a mere pittance compared with how much it cost to bring up that ghastly child!'

British Aerospace, privatized in 1984, bid for Rover in 1986. The Government was desperate to sell, and wrote off £800 million in debts to clinch the deal. Lord Young said nobody else was interested — to furious denials from four organizations. The *Guardian* revealed that an extra £38 million in inducements had been concealed from Brussels, which policed such deals to stop unfair competition. Young's reputation plunged, already muddied by refusal to intervene in the Al Fayeds' dubious Harrods takeover.

7 December 1989

The Latest Economic Miracle — Turning Water into Champagne

Once again a national asset was sold off at a knock-down price — and immediately turned into huge profits when shares traded on the Exchange.

140

13 December 1989

44,000 thousand Vietnamese who risked their lives to reach Hong Kong in small boats were adjudged 'economic' refugees. Police in riot gear gathered up 51 in dawn raids on camps and sent them home to Hanoi.

25 January 1990

Thatcher was forced to drop her cherished football identity-card scheme when an inquiry into the crushing to death of 95 fans on the terraces of Hillsborough in April questioned its safety and recommended all-seater stadia instead.

6 March 1990

Serving the public, not just in Government but through years of opposition too, did not appeal to former Cabinet ministers who could see the writing on the wall. They decided they wanted to spend more time with their families and gathered up lucrative boardroom jobs in the City.

24 March 1990

Following a lack-lustre budget by John Major, Tories trembled when Labour took the 'safe' Mid Staffordshire seat with a huge 21 per cent swing.

27 March 1990

'She can take as long as she likes — I'm only running on the spot!'

Michael Heseltine had been quietly campaigning for himself, travelling the country, accepting every invitation to local Tory gatherings — never officially challenging the leadership, but increasingly being perceived as Prime-Minister-in-waiting. His campaign was condemned as destabilizing by the establishment, while each Lawson speech urging EMS entry shook Thatcher's position.

24 May 1990

Inflation reached 9.4 per cent. The Government devoted much energy to being the opposition to the Opposition, decrying its new moderate pro-Europe policy document issued after months of deliberation.

16 October 1990

**'This is no soft option, girl —
saving up for your clothes is your
lookout!'**

To cheer up despondent Tory con-
ference-goers, Major reduced
interest rates by one per cent and
applied to join the Exchange Rate
Mechanism, denying that the move
was political. Labour's cure-all
clothes were stolen, but he paid a
heavy price in losing the power to
devalue.

19 October 1990

**'It's awfully good, Prime Minister —
but haven't we moved
on from our Red Period?'**

A Thatcher outburst that Kinnock was a 'crypto-Communist' cast doubts among even her
supporters about her self-control and future at the helm.

26 October 1990

'Just hold everything — you're all supposed to turn to stone!'

Mrs T.'s days as a roadblock to European unity were over. Euro-leaders voted for progress to economic union and a common currency by the end of the next decade by 11 votes to one.

31 October 1990

'Ah, dear boys, thank heaven I've found you — all is forgiven!'

Playing her Little England card, the Prime Minister told Parliament that future generations might accept a Euro-currency but true Brits would stick with the pound. Sir Geoffrey Howe, 'deeply anxious at the mood you have struck', resigned, saying that she would reduce Britain's influence in Europe.

9 November 1990

The Chancellor rubbed his hands in anticipation of huge savings on defence as the Cold War thawed. Cynics suspected that Thatcher hoped for salvation through a Gulf War Factor.

15 November 1990

Hostile bowling would not intimidate the Prime Minister and she would hit it all over the ground, she told the Lord Mayor's banquet. But Sir Geoffrey Howe killed her premiership with his resignation speech, which was all the more astounding coming from a mild man whose style Denis Healey likened to being 'savaged by a dead sheep'.

The struggle between the true interests of the nation and loyalty to Mrs T. had been too great — 'the time has come for others to consider their own response to the tragic conflict of loyalties which I have myself wrestled for perhaps too long'. Heseltine challenged for the leadership the next day.

20 November 1990

Tory MPs faced the horrific choice between sure electoral defeat under the leadership of Thatcher or a blue-rinse backlash in the constituencies where 'her people' were shocked at their heroine's treatment. Heseltine's lieutenants faced ordeal by de-selection.

22 November 1990

Mrs T. polled 204 MP votes to Heseltine's 152, with 16 abstentions — 4 votes too few for absolute victory under the rules. Within minutes of the result Thatcher told Paris newsmen that she would fight.

23 November 1990

A trail of ministers headed to Downing Street to offer their advice. Support for Mrs T. was eroding and at a 9 a.m. Cabinet meeting she announced her withdrawal from the contest, allowing enough time for Hurd and Major (her apparent choice) to stand. Tebbit declined. In a bravura performance, Thatcher proudly trumpeted her achievements in her last speech during that afternoon's no-confidence debate and was cheered by Tories. Major scored even fewer votes than Thatcher — 185 to Heseltine's 131 and Hurd's 56 — but his opponents conceded defeat and a third ballot was avoided.

POLL TAX — THATCHER'S FOLLY

The Community Charge   *18 November 1987*

Thatcher pledged in 1974 that she would abolish rates and the Government now announced that a poll tax would be introduced in England and Wales on 1 April 1990. Scotland, the guinea pig, would receive it earlier.

18 December 1987

Many Tories recognized the injustice of a millionaire paying the same tax as his chauffeur, and predicted that the complicated new system would cost more to administer. Heseltine, Ted Heath and Sir George Young vigorously opposed it in the Commons, wanting a system reflecting ability to pay. In Scotland, 'can't pay, won't pay' disobedience was threatened.

23 May 1988

Attempts in the Lords to make the tax fairer were flattened by use of a three-line whip (a compulsory 'yes' vote) and the summoning of dozens of 'back-woodsmen' peers not normally known for their attendance in the House.

27 February 1990

'Oh yeah? Let's see your car do better in here — if you have one!'

Labour and Tory councils alike capitalized on the new system to set much higher poll-tax rates than optimistic Government estimates. The new tax was disapproved of by 73 per cent of voters. Tory chairman Baker mocked Labour's unstated alternative. The following month 300,000 protesters gathered in Trafalgar Square. The rally degenerated into a riot with cars and buildings burnt and shops looted.

4 April 1990

'On second thoughts, we can't leave vital issues to gullible idiots like you!'

The poll tax's premise was that high-spending councils, presumably Labour, would be answerable to ratepayers at local election time. Chris Patten destroyed the accountability theory by leaping in before poll day to cap the rates declared by 20 councils – none of them Tory, although excessive spending did exist in 'blue' areas.

1 May 1990

Thatcher admitted that alterations to the poll tax were possible, but blamed Labour councils for the high bills. Nevertheless, Labour enjoyed an 11 per cent swing in the local elections. Tory flagships Wandsworth and Westminster, which had sacrificed local services for low tax, enjoyed huge support and Baker claimed moral victory.

11 May
1990

New Broom Salesman

Heseltine urged big changes to the poll tax, and by implication suggested himself to carry it out. Thatcher was unimpressed.

20 July
1990

'Agreed then — we give him something to chew on until we make land!'

With one in five avoiding paying their poll tax the Tories panicked. Casting an eye towards a forthcoming election, they decided to throw money at the problem.

LABOUR PAINS

9 July 1970

'Heir today, gone tomorrow — eh, Roy?'

A prophetic cartoon, as Roy Jenkins became Deputy Leader of the Labour Party.

Trouble Brewing in Labiza   *21 July 1971*

In June, terms were agreed by Heath for Britain's entry to Europe. In the absence of a national referendum, Labour obliged by tearing itself to picccs. At a special conference Wilson waited to see the wind direction, but Jenkins, a heart-felt European, gathered George Thomson, Harold Lever and Michael Stewart as principle 'pro' allies. Jim Callaghan, Peter Shore and Barbara Castle spearheaded the 'antis', reflecting opinion-poll and trade-union feeling. (Spanish police dealt ruthlessly with hippy drop-outs in Ibiza at the same time.)

'Sam, Sam, pick up tha' musket!' *22 July 1971*

Jenkins was not for turning in his belief in Europe.

6 October 1971

'Good heavens! Look at your clothes, Roy — is this some kind of joke?'

The conference of the party which had initiated the application to enter Europe voted against entry by five votes to one, leaving an unrepentant Jenkins stranded. 69 Labour rebels voted with Heath to approve the terms of entry by 356 votes to 244. Britain joined the EC in February 1972.

5 October 1972

In April Jenkins said goodbye to leading Labour and resigned (along with Lever, Thomson and David Owen) from the Shadow Cabinet after it voted for a referendum on continued membership of the EC, the brainchild of new Party President, Tony Benn. At the Party Conference Benn sought to punish the treachery of the 'pro' rebels, but was foiled. (Dick Taverne left the party and re-won his seat as a Democratic Labour candidate.)

26 May 1977

'Try to forget about them — they'll move on.'

Extremist Trotskyite factions moved into the Labour Party and, taking advantage of constituency apathy, took over a number of key positions.

A Campaign for More Representative Icebergs *1977*

The Trotskyites' campaign was to reduce the cosy power of the Parliamentary Labour Party and make it follow policy dictated by constituency workers.

2 October 1979

Under Benn's leadership the Left went from strength to strength and demanded a party over-haul, in particular the method of selecting the leader.

3 October 1979

The Parliamentary Labour Party could only gape as Benn and a Left-dominated National Executive Council with youthful, activist local support soared even higher into a socialist dreamland. Reg Prentice quit to join the Tories, and David Owen, Bill Rodgers and Shirley Williams surveyed the scene with gloom.

3 October 1980

The Parliamentary Party managed to cling to control of their manifesto but Labour MPs would now face mandatory reselection procedures in their constituencies. The PLP's right to select the party leader was also threatened as a more representative college of selection was investigated, probably opening the way for a Benn leadership and sabotaging Healey's hopes of power.

13 October 1980

'You've gotta be kidding — how can you run out of flying hours?'

In a pre-emptive strike, Callaghan, tired of the feuding, resigned before the Benn forces could set up the new leadership voting system.

16 October 1980

'I do believe you're right — normally it is the ship which is set alight!'

Shore, Healey, Silkin and Foot were the initial candidates as the constituencies scented betrayal.

20 October 1980

The Labour Left prodded 67-year-old Michael Foot into a caretaker and healer role. Right-wingers, contemplating leaving the party, placed their faith in Healey.

21 October 1980

'Take over will you — I've decided to make a come-back.'

Foot replaced Shore as the Left's man and in a shock result won by 139 votes to 129. Healey suspected that some who had intended to leave the party had voted for Foot to make their defection seem more plausible.

28 January 1981

'You can't have it both ways, lady — either you're one of us, or . . .'

At a special conference Labour decided that future leaders would be elected by 40 per cent union vote, 30 per cent constituency and 30 per cent MPs. It was the last straw for three former ministers — Owen, Rodgers and Shirley Williams — who joined Roy Jenkins, recently returned from being President of the European Commission, to issue the Limehouse Declaration. This document condemned Labour's new extremism and formed a 'council for social democracy' prior to floating a new party. (Williams, a member of the Labour Party National Executive, was hounded by Benn until she resigned in February.)

23 March 1981

'Now look here, Benn, get back on board immediately — you're out on a limb!'

Benn portrayed himself as the only true implementer of grass-root wishes and the PLP as betrayers of socialism.

Bennana Skin

3 April 1981

Just as Labour started to recover, Benn challenged Healey for the deputy-leadership.

5 June 1981

'That'll keep him quiet for a minute — now are you sure you know how to shoot that thing?'

Foot challenged Benn to go the whole hog and stand for his job. Benn did not oblige and Healey defeated him by the narrow margin of 50.448 per cent of the electoral college vote.

27 September 1982

Labour seemed so involved in internal squabbles that greater issues — like effectively opposing the Tories — were beyond it.

November 1981

Benn wanted compensation for Labour councillors fined after not setting rates within Tory-dictated limits. The Shadow Cabinet ruled that the law must be obeyed and Benn was cast out for violating the code of collective responsibility.

28 February 1983

'Dear oh dear, it's pitiful — I'm afraid it's time for the old nag to go to grass!'

The task of motivating a split party with a death wish was too much for Foot. It appeared that the coup de grâce would be delivered by the soaring SDP-Liberal alliance at the Darlington by-election.

14 June 1983

Labour was obliterated in the South in the General Election and Foot stood down. Neil Kinnock streaked into favourite's position with the support of top trade-unionists Clive Jenkins and Moss Evans. Foot, Healey and Silkin decided it was time for new blood, leaving Hattersley and Shore as the other contenders.

2 October 1983

'Lesson One: Take your seat at the controls — so far so good.'

41-year-old Kinnock, a left-winger, with right-winger Roy Hattersley as his deputy, took over the controls — apparently a 'dream ticket'.

165

26 July 1984

A disappointed Conservative press discovered that Kinnock was no prisoner of the Left as he skilfully outmanoeuvred Labour's National Executive.

30 September 1985

Rather as Gorbachev did later, young blood and new philosophy at the top revolutionized the party's white-haired image. But Benn, Heffer and Scargill were ready to fight any betrayal of ideals.

28 November 1985

'Frankly, Grannie, you've changed so much that I've had to call in another opinion.'

The Trotskyite 'Militant Tendency' group had taken over apathetic Labour constituencies and now controlled Liverpool council. Kinnock set out to oust the parasites and an NEC inquiry was set up.

27 February 1986

Kinnock triumphed and Liverpool militants such as Derek Hatton were driven from the party. Elsewhere the Government was doing Kinnock's work for him by surcharging and removing from public service those extremists who failed to impose Government limits on council spending.

1 October 1986

Kinnock's new crusade for morality in the get-rich-quick, mean and greedy Britain of Thatcher was unveiled.

The Blackpool Tea Party   *3 October 1986*

Although opinion polls indicated that the nation still stubbornly wished to hang on to nuclear defence, Labour voted for unilateral disarmament.

The Leader's New Clothes — (sort of)   *10 December 1986*

Labour protested that it would spend savings made abandoning nukes on a really effective conventional defence. The Tories mocked the policy as leaving Britain 'defenceless'.

16 April 1987

To the Iron Lady's horror, Labour's defence lunacy became infectious as the super-powers shed nuclear weapons in the thawing of the Cold War.

29 September 1987

The Left, so recently in control of party policy, watched in horror as Kinnock set out to capture the upwardly mobile vote, his crusade strengthened by voter rejection of Labour's official election platform.

21 June 1988

Trade unionism was impotent under Tory laws and its membership was dwindling. When Murdoch sacked old print craftsmen and introduced new technology at Wapping, electricians of the EETPU cheerfully back-stabbed their brothers and took over, signing no-strike agreements.

5 September 1988

'Aha, Brother Eric — we've just been discussing your future with this order!'

Eric Hammond and his defiant electricians were expelled from the TUC by a hostile Bournemouth Congress.

9 September 1988

Trade Unions had been excluded from any say in Downing Street decision-making. Traditionally anti-Europe, they were converted overnight when socialist EC president Jacques Delors outlined his vision of increased workers' rights after 1992.

3 October 1988

A Benn leadership challenge only served to give Kinnock an increased mandate to overhaul Labour policy, including the abandonment of unilateralism and nationalization in the next Labour Manifesto if keeping them would mean lost votes. The Left viewed his 'market economy' as a surrender to capitalism.

6 October 1988

Kinnock's sponsoring union boss, Ron Todd (TGWU), upstaged him with an attack on Labour's new direction.

172

19 May 1989

Kinnock presented his new moderate 88-page policy statement, ditching much old socialism. Tony Benn called a conference of 'true socialists' to challenge the new route.

7 September 1989

'We know it's quite a task — just rescue 'em one at a time!'

The unions and Labour sadly acknowledged that returning all Tory sell-offs to public owner-
ship would be impossible, but the TUC urged a gradual salvage of national assets essential to
the nation's security.

BREAKING THE MOULD
The Centre Parties

1969

The Liberals' constant problem was how to win a number of seats more accurately reflecting their percentage of the popular vote, and the only answer was proportional representation (PR), opposed by the big-boy beneficiaries of the first-past-the-post system.

1 March 1974

The Thing in the Middle of the Road

The Liberals collected 6 million votes in the 1974 General Election but only won 14 seats. In addition, four seats separated the big two parties — 'We are all minorities now,' said Liberal leader Jeremy Thorpe. Heath wooed Liberal support and failed.

11 May 1976

**'Thank heavens the chappie's gone —
I can't stand the smell of burning
flesh!'**

Scandal involving Jeremy Thorpe might have erupted earlier if the Liberals had propped up Heath. Rumours of a relationship with male model Norman Scott bubbled for two years until Scott allged 'persecution' in open court. Thorpe released some private letters, then resigned to the mixed relief and sadness of his party. The affair gained momentum until Thorpe was finally acquitted of involvement in conspiracy to murder.

177

The leaderless party instinctively turned to its revered past leader, Jo Grimond, as caretaker while a leadership contest was organized.

The Unpaid Piper

Under David Steel, the Liberals extended the life of a limping Callaghan government with an 18-month Lib-Lab Pact. Steel still claims that it provided a period of stability and kept inflation below 9 per cent, as socialist excesses were vetoed and Callaghan helped to control the Left. Callaghan tried to honour a pledge of PR for Euro Parliamentary elections, but could not deliver. When the Liberals withdrew in 1978, Labour carried on into the Winter of Discontent and lost the election.

26 January 1981

'. . . though she looked back, half hoping that they would call after her, the last time she saw them they were trying to put the dormouse into the teapot.'

When the exclusive right to choose a leader was removed from Labour MPs, Shirley Williams, David Owen and William Rodgers joined Roy Jenkins as a 'Gang of Four' preaching social democracy. Nine other MPs followed.

2 February 1981

'What do you mean, can't we slow down a bit? We haven't even started the motor yet!'

The four had planned to float a party in the summer but when thousands enquired about joining and opinion polls showed 38 per cent support, the Social Democratic Party (SDP) launch was brought forward to 26 March.

28 November 1981

Roy Jenkins failed to win the Warrington by-election in July, but slashed Labour's majority. In London 16 Islington councillors followed their local MP into the SDP. The Liberals swept Croydon, and in November Shirley Williams took Crosby for the SDP, demolishing a 19,000 Tory majority with a 25 per cent swing. The new party claimed that the mould of British politics was now broken.

27 March 1982

Roy Jenkins had to go north of the border to Glasgow's Hillhead ward to win a by-election, but at last the SDP leader had a seat in the Commons. Liberal-SDP Alliance support reached 55 per cent in the opinion polls.

12 September 1983

'No thanks — we both get a look in this way.'

The Falklands Factor foiled an Alliance breakthrough in the General Election of 1983. They collected 25 per cent of the vote and were runners up in two-thirds of Tory-won seats. Following the example of Labour's Michael Foot, Roy Jenkins stood aside for a younger SDP leader, David Owen, who rejected merging with the Liberals for at least five years.

13 September 1983

Owen insinuated himself between the two major parties with a combination of policies advocating a market economy, strong defence and compassion for the ill and jobless.

15 September 1983

PR was still the only way the SDP could get seats reflecting popular support, but it would be suicide for the big parties to implement it.

16 September 1986

The Liberal Party, traditionally the home of protest, watched in horror as their yuppified partners endorsed nuclear power and defence in a disciplined vote.

18 September 1986

Steel scented power in the event of a close election finish. However, getting Liberals to abandon protest and follow the SDP in thinking in terms of power was a problem.

26 September 1986

'Aaah, isn't that nice — he's wishing us luck!'

The old Liberal Party rejected its leadership and voted against nuclear deterrents and atomic power generation. Owen was displeased.

29 June 1987

The dual-leader Alliance was strained during the 1987 Election. Thatcher romped home with a huge victory because the 58 per cent votes against her were split between Labour and the Alliance. The poll was calamitous for the Centre parties, who received 23 per cent of the vote instead of 1983's 26 per cent, and also lost Roy Jenkins. Owen snarled at Steel's reflex call for merger as a route to survival.

7 August 1987

The Social Democrats eventually voted to merge with the Liberals — and Owen resigned as leader, being replaced by the uncharismatic Robert MacLennan.

The Drop-out   *1 February 1988*

Ill-feeling bubbled as the SDP put merger to the ballot, Owen having stated that he would have nothing to do with the scheme. In March the Social and Liberal Democratic Party was born and greeted as a 'fiasco' by Owen, who with John Cartwright and Rosie Barnes soldiered on as the Mark I SDP, with huge Sainsbury's financial backing.

13 May 1988

'Just because you've designed it you don't have to fly it — anyway I've run out of flying hours!'

Exhausted by years of coaxing Liberals into belief in power, David Steel quit. MacLennan happily retired to a lower profile, leaving two liberals, Alan Beith and ex-SBS commando Paddy Ashdown, to run for the leadership. Ashdown won substantially.

The initials SLD did not survive 'Salad Days' jokes, and the party called itself the Democrats to grumblings from Liberals. Belated discovery of environmental issues by Thatcher in face of a surge in the 'green' vote was indignantly repulsed by Ashdown.

24 February 1989

Squabbling Centre parties split the anti-Tory vote in the Richmond by-election where an exceptional SDP candidate might well have won.

25 February 1989

'Don't you think we should get together some time?'

Ashdown proposed a pact to avoid future vote-splitting. Owen rejected it.

23 April 1991

'A wild card? Now let me see — maybe nostalgia would haul in a good crowd!'

Owen's SDP membership dwindled and in 1990 he suffered the indignity of his candidate being defeated by Screaming Lord Sutch's Monster Raving Loony Party at Bootle. The party was wound up in June 1990 leaving Owen, Cartwright and Barnes as independents. Owen continued to score well in opinion polls and the Tory press urged him to go Conservative rather than leave politics. Preliminary negotiations were held in 1991. (Tennis champion Bjorn Borg lost his first major comeback match at Monaco.)

8 May 1991

'That seems — gulp — very reasonable. We'll bear it in mind!'

As this chapter began, so it ends, with the renamed Liberal Democrats looking as ever for a deal with someone who would provide PR. There were increasing signs of support within the Labour Party.

ULSTER.

5 August 1969

'Coming in? It's terrible!'

Sixties' protest reached Northern Ireland, Britain's sleeping dilemma. The one-third Catholic population suffered job, housing and franchise discrimination. A Civil Rights Association led by Bernadette Devlin protested against this, and for the disbandment of the hated all-Protestant B-Specials — the armed police reservists.

Marchers met with police violence and later battles with Protestant mobs. Prime Minister Captain Terence O'Neill admitted defeat and was succeeded by James Chicester Clark. Westminster was reluctantly drawn into something it would rather forget as the marching season began and riots followed riots.

14 August 1969

Londonderry Air, 1969

The streets were full of tear-gas as the Protestant Orangemen's 'Apprentice Boys' provocative march through the Catholic city of Belfast was answered with petrol bombs and snipers. The injured totalled 112 and British troops were despatched as a 'limited operation'. 'The enormity of the problem was little comprehended on the mainland,' wrote Tom Baistow in the *New Statesman,* and complained that cartoonists were trying to extract 'jokes' from the ugly situation, 'reminding us that the dailes have still not filled the vacuum left by Low and Vicky. The only drawing that got to the heart of the matter was Gibbard's . . . a couple choked with tear-gas in a ruined street'.

190

11 September 1969

The Real Belfast Wall

The B-Specials were placed under army control and disarmed, with plans for disbandment. For safety the two civilian factions erected makeshift barriers and patrolled them with vigilantes. As 7000 British troops settled in for a long stay, engineers erected an official six-foot barbed-wire wall separating the Protestant Shankhill Road from the Catholic Falls Road areas – and imposed curfews.

'Actually, it was supposed to be Satan.'

29 November 1969

Bernadette Devlin, now a 22-two-year-old elected MP, was sentenced to six months' imprisonment for inciting a riot at Bogside. When she was refused leave to appeal to the Lords, police ambushed her en route to a meeting and carried her off to prison. 1000 supporters at the meeting rioted and 20 soldiers were injured.

The army, formerly protectors, were now viewed by Catholics as an imperialist tool, and they turned to the previously emasculated IRA for defence. The campaign of murder provoked Protestants to set up their own terrorist gangs. South of the border, Irish ministers Charles Haughey and Neil Blaney were dismissed when charged with illegal gun-running but acquitted on a murky defence that it was an official intelligence operation.

4 September 1971

The Government introduced internment and 342 suspected IRA members were imprisoned without trial. Many were innocent. All marches apart from Remembrance Day were banned. Membership of the Provisional IRA soared as it split from the old IRA and promised a mainland bombing campaign. Ireland was the safe haven for attacks on British troops.

19 September 1971

'Aggressor! How dare you stand between me and my destiny!'

The amiable Reginald Maudling, then Northern Ireland Secretary, could do nothing to prove Britain's good intentions.

29 September 1971

'We agree that we all deplore fire — and we'll ring each other up when we get any bright ideas on how to put it out!'

Ireland's Prime Minister Jack Lynch saw Protestant-Catholic power-sharing as the only solution to the bloodshed, while Ulster's William Faulkner favoured more say in government for Catholics and housing reform. But both were too late — the question had moved on from reform to the dream of a united Ireland.

19 October 1971

The wearing of black hoods, enforced standing for hours during interrogation, and the use of noise and sleep-deprivation were revealed by the Compton Inquiry, which rattled the British Government. In London an IRA bomb destroyed the observation platform of the Post Office Tower.

24 December 1971

'Nothing to worry about — just hold it steady, will you?'

Jack Lynch was uneasy about an electoral backlash if Ireland fully cooperated with Britain in a cross-border crackdown on the IRA.

2 February 1972

On 30 January itchy-fingered British paratroops shot 13 dead in Londonderry during an anti-internment march defying the ban on demonstrations.

In retaliation, the IRA vowed to kill as many soldiers as possible and the British embassy in Dublin was burned down by angry crowds. Ireland broke off diplomatic relations with Britain and Heath realized that something had to be done.

After civilians were killed and maimed by bomb explosions in Aldershot and London, Heath imposed direct rule from Westminster for at least one year while he tried to get both sides talking. The Unionists called it betrayal.

When Irish Eyes are Smiling *9 March 1973*

Unionists held a general strike, closing down industry, electricity and transport and supervised by masked men. Petrol bombs closed shops that ignored the call. Bomb blasts outside the Old Bailey and the Ministry of Agriculture shook London, leaving one dead and 250 injured.

21 May 1974

Northern Ireland Secretary William Whitelaw succeeded in setting up a power-sharing executive in December 1973. London, Belfast and Dublin agreed to a Council of Ireland to consider common problems. Ireland could unite if Ulster voted for it, but not otherwise. Security and law and order remained Whitehall's responsibility. However, the Northern Ireland Assembly was made unworkable in quick time by Ian Paisley's Protestants. Faulkner and the executive resigned after a seven-day general strike.

The Other Maze Prison　　　*9 December 1980*

Thatcher, having lost her close aide Airey Neave to a House of Commons car-park bomb-attack in 1979, looked for fresh solutions to the festering problem of bombings, murders and hunger strikes. A high-profile delegation of Prime Minister, Chancellor, Foreign Secretary and Northern Ireland Secretary went to Dublin. Thatcher was not amused by Haughey's public hint of major changes to north-south relations in the future.

In the H-blocks of Belfast's Maze Prison 'on the blanket' strikes by IRA suspects, naked apart from a blanket, and living in filth, escalated to hunger strikes to secure 'political status' and immunity from prison work.

11 December 1980

Hunger strikers asked for food, apparently after intervention by Haughey, now Irish PM. Both Unionists and the Opposition suspected shady deals between Dublin and Whitehall.

15 November 1985

'As far as I can make out, Messrs Paisley and Powell are stating that they refuse to have their destiny influenced by a foreign power!'

Thatcher withstood hunger-strike deaths, bomb massacres of horseguards and bandsmen in London and her own narrow escape in an IRA bomb attack on the Grand Hotel in Brighton, and rejected unification, confederation or joint authority as solutions.

Warm relations with new Irish leader Dr Garet Fitzgerald led to an Anglo-Irish Agreement. Ireland abandoned claims to the North but gained a consultative role on security, legal and political matters and a part in an intergovernmental secretariat in Belfast. Thatcher's close adviser, Ian Gow, resigned in protest, and was killed a few years later by a bomb under his car.

Unionists were furious at a foreign power having a say in their affairs. The mainland smiled grimly, having just been informed that in the event of war Britain's Cruise missiles would be under American control.

16 November 1985

'I'm afraid they're hard of hearing — all I said was that we would be putting our new guest in the Annexe!'

Betrayed by one of their own, furious Unionists marred the first conference with clashes, leaving 31 police injured. Anglo-Irish relations became icy as one by one British extradition orders were refused by Irish courts, either through faulty procedure or rulings that fair trials could not be expected in Britain. The Agreement continued, however, and was endorsed when Haughey returned to power.

10 November 1987

The IRA scored a bloody own goal when a bomb killed 11 and badly injured 63 at the Inis-killen Remembrance Day parade to honour World War dead. The IRA apologized while blaming army high-frequency scanners for triggering the explosion.

19 October 1989

The Guildford Four, convicted on police lies and forced confessions for a 1975 pub bombing, were eventually released by the Court of Appeal. The Birmingham Six were released in 1991 after forensic evidence was discredited and lies and tampering with evidence by police was proven.

5 July 1990

'Terribly sorry about this — her mother wants to be involved!'

Patient efforts by new Northern Ireland Secretary Peter Brooke appeared to bear fruit as Unionist-Catholic talks about future self-government seemed likely — until Dublin insisted on a seat at the table.

UNCLE SAM :
A Special Relation

VIETNAM

'... My Kingdom for a Horse!'   *2 May 1970*

After five years of military involvement in Vietnam, then Cambodia, and with a US deathroll exceeding that for the Korean War together with protests on the streets at home, Richard Nixon badly needed a victory.

8 April 1971

US morale was at low ebb after Lt William Calley was found guilty of the massacre of Vietnamese civilians at Mylai in 1968. The unlikely vehicle for a thaw in Sino-US relations appeared in the form of an invitation to play table-tennis — 'ping-pong diplomacy'.

The Red Carpet   *17 July 1971*

Nixon accepted that Taiwan could no longer be the 'official' China and accepted a visit to Peking to face Mao, the containment of whose ideology (the Domino Theory) had drained so much US manpower and hardware. In October, Chiang Kai-shek's Nationalist China was expelled from the United Nations and replaced by Peking.

February 1972

'Great news, fellers! We didn't need to contain those Commies after all!'

Nixon enjoyed a triumphant visit to Peking. The only stumbling-block was Chinese insistence that he should no longer recognize the Taiwan regime if he wished to begin diplomatic relations.

3 May 1972

'If this boy of yours can look after himself, how come you've gotta wind him up all the time?'

Nixon, desperate to have his boys home, was exasperated by the failure of the South Vietnamese to withstand the North's onslaught. The last US ground combat troops left Vietnam in August 1972 at the final cost of 45,000 dead. Nixon won a second term and bombing carried on until a ceasefire agreement was reached in Paris on 23 January 1973 and prisoners of war were exchanged with a triumphant Hanoi.

WATERGATE

'My goodness! Fancy that!'

Five men, including the Nixon re-election committee security coordinator, were arrested in the Watergate offices of the Democrats in Washington, carrying sophisticated bugging equipment, on 17 June 1972. Nixon's campaign manager, John Mitchell, resigned in July. Two former White House aides, Hunt and Liddy, were charged with conspiracy and four top Nixon aides, Haldeman, Ehrlichman, Kleindienst and Dean, resigned. On television Nixon accepted responsibility but denied personal involvement in a burglary or a cover-up.

28 April 1973

John Dean, legal counsel to the President, said that he would not be made a scapegoat. With investigative journalists of the *Washington Post* and *New York Times* digging deep, the scandal was unstoppable.

2 May 1973

2 June 1973

The Senate select committee investigating the affair was headed by Senator Sam Ervin. Nixon finally admitted a cover-up but would not be interrogated. Dean revealed that Haldeman and Ehrlichman were the masterminds of the cover-up of the break-in and several other illegal acts which were a cancer to Nixon's presidency.

The battle centred on the revelation that secret listening devices had recorded all conversations in the Oval Office. The Senate committee and the Attorney-General's special prosecutor, Archibald Cox, were determined to hear whether the President had told the truth. Nixon refused to hand over the tapes.

12 October 1973

Vice-president Spiro Agnew was investigated by a Federal Grand Jury for bribery, extortion and tax fraud. Nixon distanced himself and Agnew resigned, admitting tax evasion, and was succeeded by Gerald Ford.

Nixon ordered the Attorney-General to sack Cox, which he refused to do and resigned. His deputy also refused and it was left to the Solicitor-General to sack Cox. The President eventually consented to release the tapes to Judge Sirica. Sadly 18 minutes were missing through the 'terrible mistake' of Nixon's secretary pushing the wrong button.

2 May 1974

The Incredible Shrinking President

The House of Representatives' judiciary committee considered impeachment proceedings against the President after a Federal Grand Jury ruled that Nixon had been involved in the Watergate cover-up conspiracy. Also impeachable was his refusal to hand over additional tapes, and in July the Supreme Court ruled that he must hand them over for evidence in the trial of his aides. Nixon claimed 'executive privilege' and the House judiciary voted for impeachment.

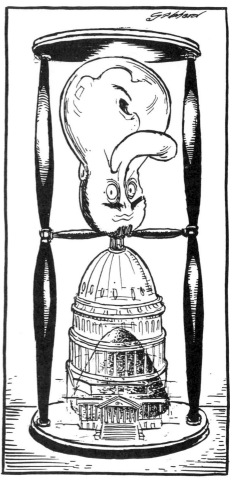

7 August 1974

'Can't we still turn this thing upside down?'

Faced with impeachment, Nixon tried to play for time.

208

Rather than be impeached, Nixon resigned and was succeeded by Ford, the man nobody had voted for.

Ford pardoned Nixon, believing the ex-President had suffered enough, and hoping to end the continuing atmosphere of witch-hunt.

17 September 1974

'He looked so sad without his feathers . . . I let him go!'

7 November 1979

Millions marched in Iran demanding the Shah's abdication after strikes and rioting. The Shah and his family fled to Egypt. The Ayatollah Khomeini, a fundamentalist Muslim, returned from fourteen years' exile in Paris and imposed strict Islamic law and established a republic.

President Jimmy Carter became an innocent victim when the Shaw flew to the US for an operation. Mobs seized the US embassy in Tehran and took staff hostage to force the hand-over of the sick former ruler.

*9 April
1980*

The Shah went into exile in Panama, then, as Iran sought extradition, fled back to Cairo. 53 Americans remained hostage, ostensibly to students, but in fact to the Ayatollah, who refused to let a UN commission see them unless its members expressed a view about the crimes of the Great Satan (America) and the Shah.

The world quaked as Carter became increasingly demented by the sight of a Third World country holding the mightiest of nations to ransom.

On 25 April 1980 a John Wayne-style rescue went horribly wrong. Carter took personal responsibility for the loss of eight lives when a helicopter and a tanker aircraft collided over the desert sands during a clandestine rescue bid. Fears grew that, encouraged by the hawks, Carter would attempt something bigger. The efficiency of the British SAS in clearing gunmen from the Iranian embassy in London was galling.

6 November 1980

'Tough, but that's show-biz, bud — anyway, once I've put in a bit of gun-play and chucked out all that brotherly love crap, we might have us a movie!'

A humiliated US turned against Carter and voted in former movie actor, Ronald Reagan. Eleven years later there were rumours that Republicans encouraged Iran to delay releasing hostages until after the election.

19 January 1981

The 'do-good' president was replaced by a 'feel-good' one, and the Ayatollah heaped on the humiliation by delaying the hostages' release until Reagan was inaugurated.

15 August 1981

The new president was shot in March by John Hinckley III, and recovered. He in turn assassinated Brezhnev's cordial peace overtures and then wondered at the cool response to his own initiative.

213

18 February 1985

Brezhnev died in 1982 and the USSR was ruled by Andropov then Chernenko. Reagan, meanwhile, drifted further into comic-book land, naming the Soviets an 'Evil Empire' and insisting on a space-based laser and missile defence screen over the USA, dubbed 'Star Wars'. Allied opposition was muted by lucrative offers of research-and-development contracts.

A domestic boom saw Reagan win a second term in 1984. A new era was born with the arrival of 54-year-old Mikhail Gorbachev at the Soviet helm, culminating in a Geneva summit in November 1985.

14 April 1986

Using the bombing of a Berlin discotheque as an excuse, Reagan bombed Libya, the paymaster of international terrorism. The adventure was fiercely opposed in Europe (which would suffer terrorist vengeance), but supported by Thatcher, who permitted the use of US F-111 aircraft based in Britain.

16 April 1986

'Heh! Heh! That goddam insect'll think twice before he stings peace-lovin' folk again!'

Three British hostages in Lebanon were murdered in retaliation and en masse all US travellers stayed at home, but the expected back-lash was muted, as was Gaddafi's future role.

13 October 1986

At their second summit in Iceland, Reagan and Gorbachev started well with agreement to remove interme-diate nuclear forces from Europe and to reduce strategic weapons, until everything was stalemated by Reagan's refusal to abandon 'Star Wars'.

'Hey, don't get the wrong picture, pardners! There are some helluva nice guys in the tribe who are prepared to give back Jimmy Carter's scalp!'

The White House insisted that the release of an American hostage in Beirut by Terry Waite, the Archbishop of Canterbury's envoy, had not involved any deals. However, Reagan was forced to admit to eighteen months' secret diplomacy with Iran and the authorizing of sales of arms in exchange for the release. He argued that the deals strengthened the hand of moderates in Tehran who might soon rise to power. Waite himself was kidnapped two months later.

The 'Teflon Presidency', which had sailed unscarred through many a crisis, came to grief as the President pleaded ignorance of details — like the transfer of the $30 million profit on the deal to the Contra rebels trying to overthrow the democratically elected left-wing government of Nicaragua. (Congress had refused to provide funds for the fight.)

The Rime of the Ancient President   *27 November 1986*

The US administration drifted aimlessly as a befuddled President saw his National Security adviser John Poindexter and Security Council aide Lt-Col. Ollie North resign. The scandal earned the name 'Irangate'.

2 March 1987

In a damning report, the commission of inquiry headed by Senator John Tower ruled that Reagan had not deliberately misled the people but had made mistakes and seemed unaware of what was going on. Reagan's chief-of-staff, Donald Regan, was blamed for the chaos. The Evil Empire came to the rescue with fresh offers of nuclear disarmament.

The True Confessions of Rip Van Washington   *6 March 1987*

Reagan's relaxed life-style, afternoon snoozes, inattention to detail and possible approaching senility caused concern in the outside world, but not too much in the US where he remained popular.

All Quiet On the Western Front   *13 April 1987*

Impatient with American dithering, Gorbachev issued another challenge by offering to remove all Soviet short-range missiles from Eastern Europe in exchange for a medium-range agreement. This was much more than Reagan or his cold-warrior ally Thatcher wanted.

The Iron Lady

'The buck stops with me,' said Poindexter at the Irangate hearing. North became the nation's All American Hero as he defended himself with patriotic noises. Thatcher rescued Reagan's besmirched reputation with enthusiastic praise.

9 December 1987

The Congressional report on Irangate ruled that if Reagan did not know what was going on, he jolly well should have. Once again Gorbachev rescued the President by visiting Washington and signing a treaty to dismantle all medium- and short-range missiles.

11 December 1987

'We had full and frank discussions — and you can bet I told him about the weakness of his system!'

Neither Reagan nor Thatcher could resist lecturing Gorbachev on human rights and the evils of the Communist system. The pitfalls of capitalism were amply demonstrated by Wall Street's second crash of that year.

And they all lived happily ever after . . .

The Reagan years limped to their conclusion, marred by Donald Regan's revelations that Nancy's astrologer virtually ruled the White House. Vice-President Bush fought the Democrat's Michael Dukakis, who had won the primaries after an unexpectedly hard fight with black clergyman, Jesse Jackson, and promised tough action against the US's horrific budget deficit. America voted for its pocket and against tax increases and 'liberalism' — and for the gruesome prospect of J. Danforth Quayle a heart-beat away from the presidency.

THE THIRD WORLD

THE MIDDLE EAST

18 June 1969

'Of course all my customers give their word as gentlemen that the guns won't be used against anybody.'

The arms business was seen as salvation for an economy struggling for overseas exchange, but a terrible price was to be paid as Third World nations squandered precious wealth on huge armies.

30 September 1970

Three hijacked airliners were blown up by Palestinian guerrillas on Jordan sands after the West acquiesced to their demands for the release of PLO terrorists imprisoned in Europe.

In Cairo, Nasser sadly witnessed the disintegration of the Arab world and chaired a meeting agreeing that PLO guerrillas would get out of Jordan (their Black September). The following day Nasser died and was succeeded by the moderate Anwar Sadat.

4 February 1971

After years of cheap petrol, the mainly Arab oil-producing countries recognized their power and threatened to increase prices without consultation.

Boot-filling in the Arab World *July 1971*

The Arab world erupted in anarchy. King Hassan of Morocco crushed a coup, the Jordanian army attacked PLO guerrillas, General Numeiry of Sudan was deposed then counter-deposed the coup leaders, and Sadat also foiled a coup and purged his opponents.

17 October 1973

'Black September' PLO guerrillas burst into the Israeli team's headquarters at the Munich Olympics, killing two athletes. Nine further Israeli hostages and four terrorists were killed later when a rescue attempt with snipers was badly executed at the airport. Three surviving terrorists were released in October when a Lufthansa flight was held to ransom. In the meantime, the Great Powers took sides and poured arms and aid into the Middle East.

18 November 1977

Following the Yom Kippur conflict, Egypt lost the appetite for war and in an historic move Sadat accepted an invitation to visit Israel and address the Knesset, where he declared that he wanted a permanent Middle East peace.

September 1978

'Hm, quite promising so far — but aren't there some pieces missing?'

At Camp David Jimmy Carter brought Sadat and Begin together to sign a peace treaty. Israel promised to return the Sinai, occupied since the 1967 Six Day War, and to recognize the legal rights of Palestinians. There was, however, no undertaking to withdraw from Arab land on the West Bank and Gaza Strip. The PLO threatened Sadat's life and Egypt was expelled from the Arab League.

21 June 1982

'And so, Mr Reagan, in the words of the ancient rabbi, cleanliness is next to godliness!'

When the Israeli ambassador to London was shot and seriously wounded, Israeli jets bombed guerrilla targets in the Lebanon in retaliation. Then 20,000 Israeli soldiers crossed the border and invaded Lebanon, to the disapproval of the Americans.

31 August 1983

Following the death of his wife, Begin resigned, leaving unresolved a withdrawal from Lebanon and the future of the West Bank, now being 'settled' by the growing Israeli population and destined to be a stumbling-block to all future peace moves.

AFRICA

17 October 1970

Seeing a Soviet naval buildup in the Indian Ocean as a threat to trade routes, Heath and his Foreign Secretary, Lord Home, disregarded all opposition, and relations with Black Africa and the Commonwealth, to sell arms to South Africa.

23 October 1970

Black Africans, smarting under the tyranny of apartheid, were less impressed by the threat of Communist oppression than were the British with their huge investments in Africa's white nations.

227

5 August 1976

Relieving the Pressure

South Africa's President Vorster ordered security forces to restore order 'at all costs' when the black townships erupted into violence after the Transvaal ruled that black secondary schools must use English and Afrikaans equally as languages of tuition. Afrikaans was hated as the language of oppression. Many died as police opened fire into crowds in Soweto and the violence spread to Cape Town and Johannesburg.

4 September 1976

'I see dark strangers — and apart from that you don't seem to have any future at all!'

US Secretary of State, Henry Kissinger, warned South Africa that it must move towards a more democratic system of government, reflecting the needs of its huge majority of blacks. Ominously for South Africa, Ian Smith in breakaway Rhodesia announced a two-year transition to black majority rule.

9 June 1977

The Commonwealth Conference warned White Africa to change its repressive system or face terrible bloodshed.

13 August 1979

'Good grief, Mr Smith — whatever will the natives think!'

Britain's first civic beach for nude swimming was opened near Brighton. In Rhodesia, whites followed Smith in voting for a constitution which would lead to black domination. Bishop Muzorewa, the acceptable face of black power, was elected premier in April but after meetings in Lancaster House guerrilla leaders Mugabe and Nkomo returned from exile and Mugabe was elected President.

Blowing Out the Candles   *22 March 1985*

Seventeen blacks were shot dead by South African riot police at Langa township, twenty-five years after the Sharpeville massacre of fifty-six black protesters.

15 August 1985

'Believe me, man, I do sympathize with your position — what say I bring the carrot a bit closer?'

Under P.W. Botha some restrictions were lifted, including bans on mixed marriages. But widely expected further big changes were postponed after riots and right-wing protest. The South African economy, meanwhile, began to feel the pinch as international finance withdrew its support and the US House of Representatives voted to impose sanctions.

Sitting on the Fence   *18 June 1986*

South Africa imposed a State of Emergency to forestall violence on the tenth anniversary of Soweto. A Commonwealth report by a fact-finding group of Eminent Persons reported there was no alternative to concerted international sanctions, and predicted a bloodbath if reforms were not carried out. Thatcher loudly opposed sanctions, condemning the comfortably off liberal consciences for wishing to sentence a black labour force to certain unemployment. The Opposition preferred to see this as Thatcher protecting the business interests of friends of the Tory Party.

'Splendid progress, Margaret — at last I've found somebody high up prepared to listen to your proposals on South Africa!'

The luckless Sir Geoffrey Howe burnt up air miles and suffered humiliation in both Black and White Africa bearing his mistress's message that sanctions were wrong.

15 July 1986

Thatcher's refusal to countenance sanctions ruined the Commonwealth Games in Edinburgh, which was boycotted by most of Black Africa. It also split the Tories and had the Commonwealth seething — the Queen was rumoured to be displeased.

21 July 1986

'. . . And in the purple corner, ladies and gentlemen, a surprise heavyweight contender. . .'

The *Sunday Times* went so far as to announce that the Queen wished it to be known that she was outraged at the effects of Thatcherism, particularly on Commonwealth unity. This dramatic constitutional confrontation was false, but many subjects viewed Thatcher's increasing use of the royal 'we' and her regal manner with concern.

4 August 1986

In the end, surprisingly, Britain supported a European ban on South African coal, steel, iron and krugerrands, and undertook to encourage voluntary boycotts of tourism and investment. The outlook for black Africans looked grim.

24 November 1987

Crop failures, drought and war led to famine in Ethiopia which, despite Live Aid fundraising of £50 million, showed no end. While Africa starved, the Common Market obscenely created elaborate incentives to encourage farmers to produce less food in order to relieve the strain on storage space and maintain prices.

4 July 1990

The Man She Could Do Business With

The thirty-year ban on the African National Congress was lifted by South African President F.W. de Klerk, who in February released Nelson Mandela, a political prisoner for twenty-seven years. The ANC deputy-leader was fêted internationally and optimism soared as the ANC and the government seriously negotiated South Africa's future. Some could scarcely believe their ears when Mandela at last met Thatcher and saluted her as 'an enemy of apartheid and all kinds of racism'. Mandela wanted sanctions maintained but Thatcher insisted that de Klerk's reforms needed encouragement.

* * *

13 February 1980

'Upon my word — the only solution to the distressing misery of this poor shopkeeper is self-evident! He and yonder oil merchant must give these lowly beggars a share of their profits that they may make a habit of purchasing his goods.'

Two worthy ex-leaders, Willi Brandt and Ted Heath, surveyed the poverty of the Third World together with the woeful state of Western capitalism and deduced that if the better-off sacrificed a little wealth it would prime the pump to convert impoverished regions into consumer states and help the world go round.

12 October 1980

The time bomb was the huge debt burden and grotesquely high interest rates being carried by the Third World to the profit of Western banks.

Having had to surrender its Sahara sands, France turned to its tropical territories to test its Bomb (Force de Frappe), ignoring the loud opposition of the native peoples who lived in the region.

27 August 1985

'And so, messieurs et mesdames, 'aving revealed all, we wish you Bon Soir!'

Irritated by unwelcome attentions of Greenpeace protesters in the Pacific, frogmen were sent by France to sink their ship, *Rainbow Warrior,* tied up at its Auckland wharf. One man was killed. France confessed but the Tricot inquiry left many questions unanswered. The Defence Minister, Hernu, resigned and two French secret agents who had been arrested in New Zealand were sentenced to ten years' imprisonment. France put pressure on New Zealand to permit the sentence to be served in French territory in the Pacific, and later, magically, on health grounds, the two had to return to France.

IRAQ AND RUIN:
The Gulf War

23 October 1990

Iran was having financial difficulty in recovering from the prolonged and bloody war with its neighbour Iran. It therefore turned its attention to its former loyal ally, Kuwait, and accused it of theft of oil from disputed border fields and overproduction at the cost of Iraq's economic recovery.

Meanwhile, under military threat from Iraq, the other Gulf oil states voted to put up OPEC oil prices and reduce production.

On 2 August Saddam Hussein's huge Iraqi army invaded Kuwait. The UN Security Council swiftly authorized a blockade, or military action if diplomacy or sanctions did not remove the invader. However, Iraqi forces continued on to the Saudi border and Saddam defied UN resolutions by annexing Kuwait and calling on all Arabs to rise against America and Zionists. The Arab League, however, demanded a withdrawal.

US troops were then despatched to protect Saudi Arabia, to the horror of the Islamic world. British forces quickly followed and ultimately thirty-eight nations, including a number of major Arab states, contributed to the UN force. To protect his back, Saddam wrote off a million deaths during the eight-year war with Iran as history, and made peace with his neighbour.

While the Coalition nations waited for economic sanctions to take effect the spotlight turned onto thousands of Westerners trapped in Kuwait. Women and children were permitted to leave after three weeks but the world was outraged by a 'human shield' policy of accommodating many hostages next to strategic targets.

A constant stream of VIPs queued for audiences with Saddam to plead, sometimes successfully, for the release of their nationals, and also to find out what made the dictator tick. Ted Heath earned the ire of Thatcherites by independently negotiating for forty-eight hours for the release of 200 Britons. He actually returned with thirty-three and the promise of more later.

*15 January
1991*

The United Nations' deadline for Iraqi withdrawal expired and the stream of visitors to Saddam concluded with Perez de Cuellar, the UN Secretary-General. Kuwait had now became the nineteenth province of Iraq.

16 January 1991

The world faced the grim conclusion that war was inevitable, although in Britain the Opposition hoped that sanctions could be given longer to bring Iraq to its knees. The PLO, who saw Saddam as their last salvation, were expected to bring the fight to the streets of Europe.

18 January 1991

Suddenly it all started. The biggest army assembled since the Second World War waited patiently in the desert while a mighty air force and Cruise missiles hammered Baghdad and other strategic targets.

To demoralize the West, obviously maltreated captured US and British airmen mumbled their regrets on Iraqi television. World anger increased with the news that POWs would be housed next to bombing targets. Iraqi Scud missiles landed in Saudi Arabia, and the world held its breath as Saddam directed his missiles at non-participant Israel in an attempt to provoke retaliation and weaken the resolve of Arab Coalition members. The huge Iraqi air force stayed hidden in bunkers, or sought haven in Iran.

23 January 1991

Iraq deliberately set fire to oilfields to create a smokescreen and released a huge ecologically disastrous oil slick into the Gulf — a modest foretaste of horrors yet to come. Meanwhile, as billions poured into the war, a short distance away in the Horn of Africa famine worsened.

15 February 1991

Reflecting the national mood of reluctant support for a just war, the Labour Party offered statesmanlike low-key support. But the direct hit on a Baghdad civilian air-raid shelter caused huge casualties and horrified the Labour Left, who predicted a catastrophic conclusion to the conflict. The Allies also braced themselves for Saddam's nuclear or bacteriological weapons — or the poison gas he had already used on his own citizens, the Kurds.

21 February 1991

After a month of non-stop, mostly precision bombing watched in living-rooms the world over, Saddam and his crack troops remained underground in massive bunkers. Civilian morale was low but casualties were remarkably small. Land war, and the likelihood of massive Allied loss of life, loomed.

22 February 1991

Beacon of the Arab World

Saddam promised that a land war against his battle-hardened National Guard would be 'the mother of all battles'. Coalition commanders hoped that the destruction claimed by their air forces was correct. Meanwhile, undetected, US, British and French forces secretly moved west and prepared a flanking manoeuvre to cut off the invaders from their supplies in Iraq.

27 February 1991

The USSR, which had been out-played and deprived of any meaningful role in the conflict, tried to stop outright war, and viewed the US use of UN resolutions as a cover for an invasion of Iraq.

On 23 February Saudis and American Marines drove into Kuwait, in the pretence that this was the main attack, and liberated Kuwait City. Meanwhile, fast-moving armoured troops swept into Iraq and cut off Saddam's retreat. The manoeuvre was a great success and the largely conscript Iraqi occupation forces surrendered en masse. The road from Kuwait to Basra was choked with military and private vehicles laden with plunder and destroyed by air attack. However, the crack Iraqi National Guard remained largely undeployed. The Coalition commander, General Schwarzkopf, itched to reach Baghdad and depose Saddam but was overruled by the President.

28 February 1991

To secure a ceasefire, Iraq had to abandon all hardware taken to Kuwait and dismantle and destroy all poison-gas and nuclear-weapons production — and pay compensation. In Kuwait the oilfields had been put to the torch by retreating Iraqis and burned day and night, filling the skies with black rain. The consequences for world ecology are still incalculable.

After the ceasefire, the US forces began to withdraw as swiftly as possible — confounding all Third World cynics who had seen the war as an imperialist exercise to secure oil.

1 March 1991

There was much talk of Nuremberg-style war-crime trials. However, the real villian seemed to be Western greed for export earnings in the form of weapons of destruction for any tin-pot general prepared to pay.

'Hey, how about a little silence, folks — can't you see this baby's fighting for his life?'

Post-war euphoria and the unassailable popularity of the US President did not last long. The Shiites and Kurds took Bush at his word that it was up to the Iraqi people to rise up and overthrow the tyrant. They enjoyed early success until the rebellion was put down by Saddam's National Guard. However, there was no retreat to Kuwait for the Shiites in the South as both Iraqis and Palestinians were now tortured and victimized in a lust for vengeance in the liberated state. The Kurds, meanwhile, fled to the mountains of the North were, huddled in ravines, babies, the infirm and the hungry perished in the cold.

The celebration was spoiled. Britain and America found themselves committed to an unsought-after longer stay in the Middle East.

18 April 1991

The novice world statesman, Britain's John Major, scored his first significant victory by suggesting 'safe haven' refugee camps in Iraq, policed by Coalition troops to protect Kurds from Saddam's army. The idea was at first rejected, then implemented by Bush.

ON THE MAINLAND:
Europe in Transition.

25 April 1969

France was rocked by student riots in 1968, backed by strike action by half the workforce — but the Gaullists received their biggest vote of confidence since the war in a general election a month later. The following year President de Gaulle imperiously told the French people to vote for his proposals to abolish the Senate and reorganize regional government — or he would stand down. In the referendum 53 per cent rejected the proposals.

29 April 1969

The seventy-eight-year-old soldier-statesman resigned and returned to Colombey-les-Deux-Eglises, to die the following year. Georges Pompidou was elected his successor.

22 May 1969

One year after Russian tanks had gathered on the Czech border to express Soviet displeasure at Prague's spring of liberalism, and then invaded, Alexander Dubcek was sacked as Czech Communist Party leader. Thousands of 'anti-social' elements were rounded up and Czechoslovakia was 'normalized'. Dubcek was expelled from the party a year later.

3 February 1971

'I must say, we never had this trouble with non-Europeans.'

Ted Heath believed in Europe as a guarantor of peace and a counterbalance to the mighty super-powers. De Gaulle had blocked previous British approaches to join the EC but on 30 June negotiations really began.

France remained the stumbling block, but Pompidou could see merit in British money swelling the funds of the Common Agricultural Policy, of which France was the main beneficiary. Britain, in return, required guarantees for Caribbean sugar-producers and New Zealand farmers whose livelihoods would be imperilled. Talks became deadlocked.

7 April 1971

Frustrated by stalemate, Heath settled for the personal touch and met Pompidou.

They seek him here...

They seek him there...

Those Frenchies seek him everywhere...

Is he with Edward?

Is he with Powell?

That demmed elusive Wilson!

27 April 1971

Public opinion, which had been 71 per cent in favour of Europe in 1966, had swung the other way five years later and the unions and Labour Party grassroots members reflected the hostility. Wilson, broadly in favour of Europe, played for time and watched the wind direction.

As Heath prepared for one-to-one bargaining with Pompidou, the French expressed doubts about British commitment to the Euro concept and its willingness to say farewell to its Commonwealth and the Anglo-American special relationship.

21 May 1971

'Tell me, M'sieur 'Eath, have you ever thought of declaring your independence of the USA?'

The two leaders got on well. Heath convinced Pompidou that Britain did not intend to make trouble, and French suspicions of British attachment to Anglo-American nuclear deals became a diminishing problem as France left the NATO umbrella and developed its own Bomb.

23 June 1971

''Ave no fear, mon vieux — as promised, we are making for you the special case . . .'

New Zealand, having sacrified thousands of young men to liberate France in two wars, feared ingratitude and Prime Minister John Marshall lurked anxiously in the wings as Geoffrey Rippon negotiated an apparently fair transitional deal.

22 January 1972

Ted Heath and the leaders of Ireland, Denmark and Norway signed the Treaty of Brussels, agreeing to join the EC from 1 January 1973. (Heath's day of triumph was somewhat marred when a plastic bag of ink was thrown at him by a demonstrator against Covent Garden redevelopment.)

18 February 1972

The enabling legislation scraped through the Commons by the narrow margin of eight votes (mainly through the abstention of elderly Labour MPs) – an unconvincing demonstration of British will to play a full part in Europe. Labour promised a referendum, and in 1975 two-thirds of Britain voted to stay in.

The Mighty Sampson *17 July 1974*

Greek officers in Cyprus's National Guard ousted President Makarios and replaced him with a civilian puppet named Sampson. Turkey invaded the north to protect Turkish Cypriots, bringing them into conflict with Greek troops which had been under civilian command since the overthrow of the military junta in Athens. A ceasefire led to a new constitution which divided the country in two.

10 June 1981

A decade after the invasion of Czechoslovakia, Russia once again expressed itself unhappy with new freedom of speech and protest born this time in the shipyards of Gdansk in Poland. Familiar Warsaw Pact manoeuvres on the Polish borders hastened martial law.

'Here, want a taste?'   *30 April 1986*

Four days after the event the Soviet Union admitted to a nuclear disaster in the Chernobyl power station in the Ukraine. Radioactive fallout was recorded all over Europe, contaminating East European foodstuffs and leaving some UK sheep too radioactive for consumption. Technicians were blamed for ignoring safety rules.

12 February 1988

Mrs Thatcher became a hated figure in the Common Market as she constantly disrupted meetings with hectoring about Britain's excessive budget contributions. Meeting after meeting became bogged down on the subject of 'her' money until she won rebates. The Common Agricultural Policy, geared to preserving European farmers' standards of living through subsidy, grew ever more expensive as production outstripped consumer demand. The system's days were numbered.

19 April 1989

By lifting currency controls, Thatcher gave British investors the opportunity to put their money into the USA and other foreign centres. British industry was starved of investment, and with much trumpeting the Japanese moved in to set up factories and partnerships in an ill-disguised route to the otherwise protected European market.

255

26 April 1989

'Poor deluded fool — we've just gotta stop him before he gets frostbite!'

Gorbachev told Communist colleagues that the Party had no God-given right to rule. As the disarmament waggon rolled on, Germany, at the front line, recognized that the thaw had arrived long before the Cold War warriors of Britain and the US.

18 May 1989

'Bloody cheek! They should leave this to the police — if there were any!'

American 'Guardian Angels' vigilantes volunteered their services on London's Underground. Thatcher saw her vision of Europe as a market being threatened by a socialist vision of citizens' rights championed by EC president Jacques Delors. Labour, meanwhile, was freshly keen on Europe as perhaps the only way human rights could be preserved while the anti-Thatcher vote was split.

*27 June
1989*

**'I'll tag along behind, darlings — you wouldn't expect me to place my fate in the hands
of some foreign pilot!'**

At Bruges in September 1988, Thatcher attacked Euro bureaucracy and delay in achieving a
truly free market — but in particular the sacrifice of national identity for a United States of
Europe. As a result, she ignored the European Parliamentary elections and paid dearly, with
Labour snatching thirteen Tory seats to become the majority party.

At the Madrid summit, later, she refused to approve the Social Charter but U-turned by
indicating that Britain would join the European Monetary System — the first step on the road
to Delors' dream of a single currency and central bank — but only 'when the time is right'.
Lawson and Howe, supporters of economic union, seemed to have won.

15 November 1989

The Maggie-No Line

Gorbachev urged reforms on the aged hard-liner Honecker as East Germans voted with their feet by fleeing to West Germany via newly liberalized Hungary, Poland and Czechoslovakia. Honecker was forced to quit, but despite desperate reforms the exodus continued, culminating in first the opening, then the destruction of the hated Berlin Wall. The unification of Germany was only a few steps away.

Meanwhile, in Czechoslovakia the leadership resigned, in Bulgaria Communists lost the monopoly of power, and President Ceausescu was overthrown and later shot in Romania. The bastion of the Cold War, Mrs Thatcher, was left facing non-existent enemies.

3 November 1989

'Our alternative and evolutionary approach should now be crystal clear!'

John Major, briefly Foreign Secretary and now Chancellor of the Exchequer, proposed a 'hard ecu' currency, to run parallel with national currencies, rather than a common currency.

27 June 1990

In Dublin, Thatcher said that the Delors single-currency and central-bank plan was impossible, and insisted on sovereignty. Meanwhile, Italy summarily expelled English World Cup troublemakers.

13 July 1990

'Ah, splendid! Nicholas has unreservedly withdrawn his brick — so the matter is over!'

Nicholas Ridley, in an extraordinary *Spectator* interview, called monetary union a 'German racket' to take over Europe, adding that EC commissioners were unelected reject politicians, and the French were poodles to Germany.

As for sovereignty, 'you might as well give it to Hitler'. The Trade and Industry Secretary's outburst was later withdrawn, but Ridley had to resign, his ability to negotiate trade matters having been badly damaged.

12 March 1991

The back-bench Thatcher, having warned the world what a good back-seat driver she would be, was bounced into the cold as John Major proved to be his own man by accelerating into Europe and establishing warm relationships with Helmut Kohl, leader of the newly united Germany.

MAJOR'S ROAD AHEAD

28 November 1990

The forty-seven-year-old John Major now took the controls. By quickly conceding defeat in the less-than-decisive second ballot, Heseltine and Hurd suggested Mrs T. had company as 'back-seat driver'.

4 December 1990

'Huh! Call that an offering? Look how much *they* love me!'

Labour's worst fears were realized. Their biggest vote-winner, Thatcher, had been replaced by a grey man of humble origins who charmed both media and opinion-givers. Kinnock, fine-tuned to battle a strident Thatcher, had to amend his parliamentary style.

14 December 1990

Major's jolly pre-Party Conference wheeze of joining the ERM backfired. As the economy sank deeper into self-created recession he could no longer adjust the pound's value as the traditional remedy.

20 December 1990

'Society takes too casual an attitude to locking cars' — the Home Secretary

'Thatcher's Own' seemed disturbingly his own man, vowing to play a full part in Europe and at home showing compassion on former Thatcher battlegrounds, like increased heating allowances for pensioners in winter.

31 January 1990

To Labour's great alarm the novice leader's stature was mightily boosted by the Gulf War, with its endless opportunties to parade as a world statesman.

8 February 1991

As the Cabinet met at Downing Street, Irish terrorists fired home-made mortar bombs which, but for the intervention of a tree, would have meant certain casualties. The windows shattered, the Cabinet moved to another room to finish their meeting. All parties and the monarch vowed that terrorism would not drive the Government to a siege mentality.

5 March 1991

Labour's poll ratings had suffered during Major's Gulf honeymoon, but he cautioned euphoric Tories who wanted a June election. An angry public awaited Heseltine's review and solution to the poll-tax problem.

Getting the Message Across   *21 March 1991*

Chancellor Norman Lamont solved the immediate poll-tax problem by digging deep and providing £4.25 billion to reduce the community charge by £140, making the average bill £250. This was financed by a delayed 2.5 per cent increase in VAT, with predictable beat-the-increase spending sprees leading to increased inflation. Children would pay more for their sweets to bale the Government out of its mess, which had already cost the tax-payer £10 billion, said Kinnock.

After months of deliberation, Michael Heseltine — now Minister for the Environment — revealed a new local tax for 1993-4, still hazy in its outlines, but retaining a 'son-of-poll-tax' element in that occupants, as well as the value of the house, were taxed. The public were not impressed, and Lawson urged him to jettison anything that looked like poll tax.

When the Saints Go Marching In. . .   *25 April 1991*

Heseltine bowed to universal rejection of 'son of poll tax' by introducing the Council Tax — seven bands of tax according to the value of a house, and a 25 per cent discount if there is single occupancy. Poll tax would have to be endured until 1993, long after the next election. Ironically, on closer scrutiny it was discovered that the Tory heartland would come off worse under the new scheme as the highest band of tax was at a remarkably low level — meaning that modestly comfortable middle-class citizens would pay as much as landed gentry with huge houses — like Mr Heseltine!

5 June 1991

The Hound of the Bankervilles

Despite Government cuts in interest rates, hard-nosed banks, determined to take no risks, did not pass on these benefits to small businesses. As a result, small firms went to the wall in their thousands, deprived of financial flexibility. The Government demanded an explanation from the banks.

13 June 1991

'For heaven's sake, run for it, men — where's your Dunkirk spirit?'

European desire for swift progress to even closer economic and monetary union gained momentum, provoking hostile outbursts from Thatcher and Ridley, who saw Europe as no more than a market-place and felt that Major was swept along by the tide.

Thatcher's star had burnt out at home but in the USA, at expensive banquets to raise money for the Foundation to preserve her ideas, she bathed in adulation and sang the praises of nationhood — just as Luxemburg inserted the dread word 'federation' into a statement of Euro aspirations for agreement at the next summit.

20 June 1991

Queen Kong

Mrs T.'s loud self-pity and increasingly anti-European flailings along with her advocacy of a new trade bloc including the USA proved too much for the man she had branded a poor loser years before. Ted Heath blew his top on television and accused her of lies.

21 June 1991

While the Titans clashed, Major quietly restated that Britain was in and would remain in the Exchange Rate Mechanism, and would go no further until negotiations were finalized and Parliament had a final say.

18 July 1991

'You'll have to leave everything behind if you really want to know how to make mirrors, beads and muskets!'

Marxism died and the war of ideology ceased when Gorbachev came to London to ask the capitalist Big Seven for help in turning the USSR into a market economy. Under John Major's chairmanship the sceptical G7 offered know-how but no immediate hand-outs. Gorbachev returned to Moscow to inform the Communist Party that its future lay in social democracy, and even a change of name.

24 July 1991

The Man Who Didn't Cry Wolf

British operations of the Bank of Credit and Commerce International were closed by the Bank of England, bringing disaster to thousands of Asian shopkeepers who used it to bank their takings. Government ministers who received warnings of irregularities wriggled out of responsibility, and the Bank of England's Robin Leigh-Pemberton urbanely admitted knowledge of BCCI corruption and drugs-money laundering long before the decision — but lacked sufficient evidence to act or to warn depositors.

In a dawn raid Gorbachev's trusted vice-president Yanayev and seven other hard-liners including the Prime Minister and heads of defence, KGB and the Interior formed a State of Emergency Committee and seized power, saying the president, on holiday in Crimea, was too ill to continue. As the tanks rolled in Moscow radical resistance centred on the Russian parliament and its popularly-elected president Boris Yeltsin who, mounting a tank, told a vast crowd that the coup was illegal and called for a general strike. The shocked West halted all agreements for technical and financial aid.

21 August 1991

While Bush and other Western leaders anxiously consulted with Yeltsin by phone, and television provided live coverage, 200,000 demonstrated in Leningrad. In Moscow thousands ignored the junta's curfew to man barricades and protect the parliament building. Dissension split the KGB and the military, who were reluctant to open fire on citizens or fellow soldiers who had sided with Yeltsin, along with their tanks. One junta member retired ill and other desertions were rumoured. Finally, with bewildering speed the coup disintegrated, the tanks quit en masse and the would-be leaders fled in their limousines.

The old-guard backlash only served to strengthen the forces of freedom and democracy and seemed to be the final death of Stalinism. It made a new international giant of the hero Yeltsin while Gorbachev was restored to power, to carefully reconsider his relationship with his old adversary, now his saviour.

Gorbachev miscalculated the mood in Moscow. He did not go straight to the Russian Parliament to share their day of triumph but arrived a day later and endured some heckling and undisguised humiliation and power wielding by Yeltsin, enjoying his vengeance for past humiliation.

Under Yeltsin pressure the entire Government was sacked, the Communist Party condemned for non-intervention in the coup, and its assets seized. The Russians demanded their own army and insisted on providing key figures in the new Soviet Government.

The Baltic states declared their independence and a weary Gorbachev acquiesced. As this book's publication deadline approaches the Soviet president's days of influence seem numbered, Yeltsin is increasingly belligerent and the future outlook of the former mighty empire one of chaos and incertainty.

OUTRODUCTION

In 1969 the *Guardian* was a dream shop-window for any political cartoonist. Almost without fail each cartoon was given bold prominence on either the front or back pages.

The occupant of the cartoonist's chair for the past ten years had been Bill Papas, a flamboyant character with draughtsmanship to match. He had been David Low's chosen successor and his cartoons ranged from the whimsical in idea and execution to heart-felt outrage at racism, the Bomb and abuse of the Third World.

With great zest he reportedly swept through the newsroom, cornering journalists with the familiar enquiry: 'Any ideas?' Then, pen and nib racing across a layout pad, a splodge or two of solid black ink from a brush here and there, the cartoon would be executed, ripped from the pad, presented to the authorities and, in a puff of smoke, Bill would be off to the Savage Club or home to Canterbury.

A South African Greek, Bill was only one of a gang of Commonwealth cartoonists favoured by the *Guardian* in the post-war years. Low had been a New Zealander; Abu, an Indian, did the pocket cartoon, and after stays elsewhere in Fleet Street the Colonel Pewter strip found its ultimate resting place at the *Guardian* – if 'resting' accurately reflects the torture bearded Australian Arthur Horner went through to concoct new twists to the saga in time for deadlines while also drawing the political cartoon for the *New Statesman*.

Then, at what with hindsight seems to have been the end of an era of imported cartoonists, two New Zealanders arrived. John Kent was about to launch the trendy Varoomshka 'political strip' featuring a wide-eyed, scantily clad quick-changing blonde, who stumbled through the world of politics to the ire of feminist readers of the women's page where it found its home. And when Abu decided in 1969 to pack up the contents of his cottage in the back garden of J.M. Barrie's former home opposite Peter Pan's Kensington Gardens and to return to an editorial posting in Delhi I arrived at the *Guardian*'s door clutching a ragged bundle of sample works.

The Deputy Editor, Harford Thomas, flipped through my selection of caricatures, pocket cartoons and ornate street scenes before revealing that Abu's job had already gone to a young man with distinctive poster-style graphics, Richard Yeend.

'Have you ever thought of doing political cartoons?' Harford idly enquired. Had I what! Apparently Bill Papas had tired of his job (which also involved cartooning for the *Sunday Times* and *Punch*, as well as selling beautiful prints of scenes from the Holy Land, and fancied spending some time in the land of his ancestors, Greece. Bill badly needed a rest. 'I'd been drinking a bottle of scotch a day and not even getting drunk,' he recalled to an interviewer in 1989.

It was the classic situation of being in the right place at the right time. Harford called in the Features Editor, Peter Preston (now the Editor), who after inspecting my work agreed there was a 'Papasesque' element to my style.

'Come in after Bill goes and try your luck — we'll shoot them down in flames,' said Harford, gesturing to a framed Papas drawing purporting to be him doing just that. In this fashion the *Guardian* acquired a twenty-three-year-old political cartoonist.

Concorde 002 took its maiden flight the day I first flapped my wings. I drew Harold Wilson standing in front of the supersonic craft assuring the world that Britain would be booming henceforth. And, good heavens, it got in on an inside page. We had lift off!

Bill Papas returned six months later. He trudged up the gritty, gusty wind tunnel that was Gray's Inn Road, wearily mounted the *Guardian* steps and, he told me, thought to himself: 'Papas, you bloody fool — why have you been wasting all these years?'

It was election time and Bill hung around drawing a few cartoons and several Theodores (a comic-strip mouse with Bill's Zapata moustache and political philosophy). Having stoked up the coffers a little he about-turned and returned to Greece, finding happiness for a time with a villa, a gallery and fishing-boat, and producing handsome coffee-table books crammed with beautiful drawings of Greece and Israel. In time he tired of the life and turned his attention to America, and, admiring its dynamism, has settled in Portland, Oregon.

The *Guardian*'s readership did not automatically welcome an upstart successor to their beloved cartoonist. 'Come back, Papas — all is forgiven,' said many a letter to the Editor. An influential column in the *Bookseller* put in the boot, saying that the cartoon marred an otherwise excellent newspaper — the cutting was pointedly pinned up on the office noticeboard for all to see. With some satisfaction I received a request for an original from the article's author a few years later.

'The only plausible explanation I can think of for the lamentable Gibbard,' said my favourite offering from the Editor's postbag, 'is that Alastair Hetherington [the Editor] was left him by a long-lost aunt.'

If the editor had an aunt 12,000 miles away in New Zealand the Gibbards were too constantly on the move to have made her acquaintance. In the early days my father would buy plots of land, we'd camp on site in caravan and tent while he built a house single-handed, move into it and build another next door, sell them both and move on. School-teaching later took my parents further afield with a year and a half in Robert Louis Stevenson's Samoa, a similar period in the back-blocks of New South Wales, and a brief stay in London where I and my sketch-pads virtually lived in the South Kensington museums until Suez blew up, and the Gibbards beat a precautionary retreat back to New Zealand, via the Cape of Good Hope.

A clairvoyant whom my mother met shortly after my birth advised her to provide lots of pencils and paper. Since no further details were given, my mother

Above left. Dr Konrad Adenauer, West German Chancellor, drawn aged twelve.

Above right. Sir Edmund Hillary and friend, drawn for the school magazine in 1960, aged fifteen.

insisted at an early age that I both write and draw a record of our nomadic existence. Education on the road required that English Literature studies be illustrated by a portrait of the author, and good stories merited turning into comic strips.

But I had no real interest in cartooning until in 1957 I witnessed a young New Zealand art teacher, John Parry, drawing action-packed cartoons of soccer players to hang on the school walls in a forlorn attempt to recruit footballers in a rugby-made environment. Seeing more than normal interest from an eleven-year-old, he sent me home with bundles of drawing paper. I also took up soccer.

My parents hoped my new enthusiasm was a brief detour on the lofty road to Fine Arts. A refugee from Hungary of 1956, Franz Szirmay, who had been classically trained in Paris and Vienna, was hired to discipline my drawing and felt more strongly — 'Laz, Laz, never the caricature!'

But cartooning was irresistible, especially when it elevated you from most-caned boy of the Third Form to a creature of privilege: the school cartoonist. I was officially given a Quasimodo hideaway high among the rafters of the vast neo-Spanish building that was Auckland Grammar School and requested to decorate the gigantic school assembly hall for the annual dance. This required a huge number of black-and-white cartoons of school life measuring nine feet across and, separating them on the pillars in between, full-colour, full-length caricatures of those figures of dread, the school prefects, who all had to humbly queue up for a sitting. In addition I was excused military training and spared assemblies. Perks indeed!

A blossoming ego was suitably deflated by an audience with Gordon Minhinnick, New Zealand's best political cartoonist, who was later knighted and is now retired. The great man courteously leafed through a pile of home-produced cartoons on subjects ranging from China-India border clashes to Notting Hill riots, before gently enquiring what the punch-lines were.

At a young age I was exposed to Rule Number One. It doesn't matter how clever or even how bad the drawing is. It simply doesn't mean a thing if it hasn't got anything to say.

'Min' acknowledged the potential but said he had no plans to move on in the immediate future, and, anyway, I had a few years more of schooling ahead of me. Curses! Wouldn't anybody take on a boy prodigy so he could skip tiresome schooling and exams?

And yet, bliss. As the sky darkened over the big city buildings outside, I was permitted to sit at the great man's elbow (he drew left-handed and lettered with his right) as first he pencilled, then applied the indian ink with bold strokes of his special quill sable brush to the cartoon for the next morning's paper.

There was no doubt where my future lay. A determined self-education in how the world ticked was to follow. General elections arrived and the schoolboy with the sketchpad could be found at every campaign meeting. Elections were a popular form of entertainment in those days before television grasped the nation by the throat, and candidates' public appearances could be extremely lively and exciting. Town Hall meetings were another useful place to stalk the mighty of the city council. The massive agenda provided for visitors also provided lots of useful drawing paper.

A vocational guidance tour for schoolchildren to the Auckland *Star*, the local evening newspaper, provided an unexpected way into journalism. Only one person asked any questions, and so impressed the Assistant Editor that he was offered a job as a trainee reporter there and then. At the age of sixteen I entered the wonderful world of newspapers.

It all began rather unmagically with pushing tea-trolleys, collecting hundreds of newspapers when each different edition rolled off the presses, monitoring Press Association teleprinters and taking the office thermometer for a walk down the main street to read the midday temperature. It graduated to climbing up rope ladders to greet ocean liners far outside the harbour, recording dealings on the Stock Exchange, covering magistrates' courts proceedings (and sometimes appearing for exceeding 30 m.p.h. on the way to assignments), hobnobbing with borough mayors, covering provincial cricket matches, counting the cost of the frequent tropical storms, shark-spotting by flying-boat, and, ultimately, strolling the corridors of power in Wellington's Parliament.

As hoped for, there were many opportunties to draw cartoons and caricatures to illustrate features both on the *Star* and the student newspaper at university where I endeavoured to pursue a degree at the same time as a journalistic career. As a reporter doors opened to meet heroes of my new passion for jazz and pop, and stars like Louis Armstrong, Chubby Checker, Acker Bilk and Kenny Ball all signed their caricatures.

A spell at the New Zealand *Herald* provided the incredible opportunity to be 'apprenticed' to Minhinnick for two days of my working week when, under his

Jazzman Kenny Ball, drawn for the Auckland *Star*, c. 1963.

supervision, I was to draw cartoons for the sister weekly, the now defunct *Weekly News*.

Slowly and patiently Min moulded me, correcting my drawing, brushing up my ideas if usable and providing alternatives if not, until at long last my brain began to work. He believed that tickling was more effective than bludgeoning, and that has become my philosophy too.

Low, whose *Evening Standard* job Min had been offered before it went to Vicky, was already an idol, as were Ronald Searle and Giles. Through Min I was introduced to the works of other old masters like Phil May, the great *Daily Mail* sports cartoonist Tom Webster, Strube, Zec, the wonderful Australian draughtsman Norman Lindsay and the American creator of the Gibson Girl, Charles Dana Gibson.

Increasingly and inevitably, Gibbard style started to ape Minhinnick's so, although it was sad when I got myself sacked from the *Herald* for challenging authority, it was ultimately for the good. A spell covering the capital city for a Sunday newspaper allowed my drawing to change and my politics to develop in new directions from the somewhat returned-servicemen conservatism of most New Zealand daily newspapers. Almost alone at the time, I swam against the tide in drawing cartoons opposing any involvement in Vietnam.

After a short period hitching and occasionally working in Australia I felt myself ready for London.

*   *   *

Coming to work in England was a little like visiting distant relations. Touchingly, we New Zealanders still viewed Britain as the Mother Country. It was traditional to stand on wharfs singing 'Now is the Hour', making moist-eyed farewells to fellow youngsters as they went off on the mandatory trip to Britain and the Continent — a wild finishing school before settling down to having children and suburban delights.

Journalists were more itchy-footed than most and travelled the world, taking jobs in Australia, Hong Kong, Rhodesia, Singapore and Canada — and of course, the challenge of them all, Fleet Street. Since Britain has waved goodbye to the Commonwealth the flow has reduced to a trickle, particularly since the really big bucks are to be earned in America and Australia.

On 1 June 1967, twenty-one-year-old Les Gibbard, hard-bitten news reporter, sometime news photographer, sub-editor and cartoonist, veteran of four newspapers and one radio network, arrived as all did in those days by Greek liner at Southampton.

The thirty-foot basking shark gliding past as the ship sighted the Needles was probably an omen. All journalistic doors stayed bolted until, facing starvation, I turned to joke cartoons and sold them, primarily to the *Daily Sketch* and *Sunday Mirror.*

I consulted Keith Waite, a fellow New Zealander and cartoonist for the pre-Murdoch *Sun* and later the *Mirror,* who kindly provided a charity meal of steak, grimly outlined job possibilities and advised abandonment of my spiky signature. I did.

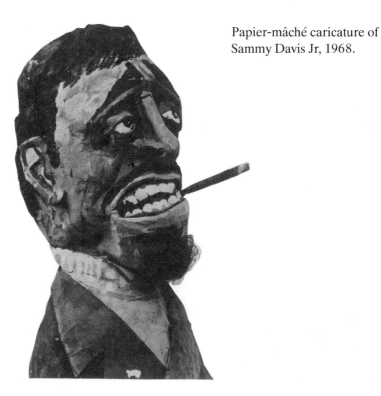

Papier-mâché caricature of
Sammy Davis Jr, 1968.

Frank Muir, published in the
Sunday Telegraph in 1968.

A chance free ticket to a press preview of the film *Doctor Dolittle* changed everything. Armed witha caricature of Rex Harrison I went looking for a market, and found the *Sunday Telegraph* arts pages, the start of a two-year relationship.

For a new arrival from the colonies it was a dream job. I started off standing on the stage of Covent Garden as Sir Frederick Ashton posed for me while Nureyev rehearsed in the background. Every week I'd sit in the dark, scribbling likenesses by torchlight at two or three film previews. Elsewhere there were dress-rehearsals, star-studded and boozy launches of TV series and plenty of free food — just as well, as my earnings remained stubbornly under the taxable minimum for two years.

There was a friendly welcome from the *Sunday Telegraph*'s editorial cartoonist, John Jensen, who was an Australian with a cartooning father. He had arrived many years before and was fortunate to do so having been locked in the ship's refrigerator for some time. Through Jensen I met the cartooning fraternity — names I had dreamed of making contact with, like Giles, Cummings, ffolkes, JAK, Dickens, Illingworth, Trog and many others, including the *Daily Telegraph*'s Nicholas Garland who knew New Zealand well, having been educated there (a useful background when it came to drawing the Barry McKenzie

Katherine Hepburn and Peter O'Toole in *The Lion in Winter, Sunday Telegraph,*
1968.

strip for Barry Humphries in *Private Eye*). On other occasions I was to run into
Pat Oliphant, the Australian who seemed to single-handedly revolutionize
United States editorial cartooning; David Low's widow and daughters; and
wandering solitarily around the Bibliothèque Nationale in Paris, Ronald Searle,
as he waited for the British Ambassador to visit an exhibition of his work.

I couldn't believe my good fortune in breaking into the *Guardian.* In 1969 it was
unlike any newspaper I had previously encountered. Word had reached us in
distant New Zealand that Lord Thomson intended to change the face of British
journalism by employing only graduates in future — and I might say it caused a
few jitters among we early school-leavers who considered ourselves graduates
of John Major's University of Life.

I had joined a newspaper already awash with Oxford and Cambridge graduates, writing like essayists rather than hacks. Here and there was a self-made
man, like Harry Jackson, last of the *Guardian* copy boys to work his way up to
the top, to 'fireman', equipped with slide rule and two passports to cover either
side of the Arab-Israeli conflicts. In general I felt considerably ill at ease, being
the product of a country with a deep-seated national inferiority complex.

The *Guardian* still boasted Alistair Cooke as American correspondent (any-
thing sent to him addressed 'Esquire' came back unopened, according to the
Editor's secretary); Philip Hope Wallace was the colossus of theatre criticism,
John Arlott covered cricket and Neville Cardus music, and it was thrilling to

hear them reminisce at *Guardian* cricket-club dinners. The Hon. Terence Prittie, originally hired to cover cricket then sent to Berlin, was diplomatic correspondent, while Norman Shrapnel wrote the wittiest of parliamentary sketches. His eventual successor, Michael White, was then slaving as a sub-editor in features, hoping some day someone would notice he could write, but Terry Coleman and Geoffrey Moorehouse were official feature-writers. Everyone wrote like a dream. Hard fact-gathering wasn't quite so popular.

My favourite character was the later-to-be-knighted Francis Boyd, a giant snorting figure with bushy eyebrows who would unsteadily lurch into the office, bellowing and glaring over his specs to do battle with the newsdesk, newly pre-sided over by a novelty, a lady News Editor, Jean Stead. The twinkle in Boyd's eye gave him away, and he was the gentlest of guides around Parliament, stopping to introduce me to passing notables like George Brown, and showing me the ropes at party conferences.

The ultimate eccentricity perhaps was the *Guardian*'s Motoring Editor, Ian Breach, who had foresworn the automobile and dedicated all available column inches to telling the public how evil the combustion engine was, and advocating the bicycle. Derek Malcolm executed an interesting double by covering horse-racing (he was a former jockey) and doing film reviews.

Fleet Street as seen by Gibbard, February 1969.

Presiding over all, with John Cole as a recently elevated deputy, was Alastair Hetherington, who had taken the helm during Suez and had lost much valuable advertising by opposing the military adventure. Boy Scoutish and rosy-cheeked, he was happiest striding the hills of border and lakes.

Most people could have earned more elsewhere in Fleet Street. The attraction was the freedom the *Guardian* offered its writers, and its independence; its fortunes being guided by a trust and its financial independence guaranteed by its profitable and grumbling stablemate, the Manchester *Evening News*, founded for that very purpose.

The *Guardian* had dropped the 'Manchester' part of its title and moved its principal parts to London, leaving a skeletal paper in the northern city under a northern Editor, Geoffrey Taylor. As I joined, that operation was being eroded and within a couple of years the old building where the legendary Editor C.P. Scott had ruled was closed down. Unlike the characterless modern office which housed the London operation here was a real newspaper office as the mind had always visualized it, full of winding wood-panelled corridors and catacombs of small offices; tangles of telephone wires cascading down from the ceiling of the newsroom.

At a farewell party attracting many who had worked there over the years, one triumphant scavenger came up with C.P. Scott's puncture kit for his legendary bicycle, hidden deep in some dusty cupboard. In a short time the historic building was demolished and gone for ever.

A Northern Features department continued to function, designing and setting pages to justify the continued employment of the Manchester composing staff. Artwork for features pages was sent up by train and came out fine. The news pages in Manchester, however, received that night's cartoon only after it had been photographed down in size and then transmitted on a photo-wire machine. Readers in the north got a very bad deal as the drawing arrived looking like it had been lifted off a 1950s television set, probably without an aerial.

Back in London the cartoon enjoyed an important role, normally occupying the top of the front page. As years went on it became even more essential as reproduction worsened dramatically. The *Guardian* did not have printing works of its own in London and used the presses of other newspapers, finally ending up with Rupert Murdoch's extremely clapped-out *Sunday Times* machines. During these terrible years the cartoon was almost the only legible form of illustration, and grown men on the photographic desk howled when their beautiful pictures ended up as grey splodges on newsprint.

Later the cartoon too was sabotaged when the *Guardian*, under its new Editor Peter Preston, moved to its very own new building, and the local authorities would not permit chemicals from the block-making processes to flow down drains. The answer was to use plastic blocks, but these too caused problems. Printers blamed the blocks, block-makers blamed the printers for incorrect paper tension. Whoever's fault it was, great black smudges would appear in any area of white in a cartoon. The only solution was to fill every available blank space with cross-hatching. (My style varies considerably throughout this book according to the kind of reproduction problem I was encountering at the time.)

Guardian Political Cartoonist's studio, c. 1970.

For the first two weeks of my *Guardian* career I was the proud occupant of a little office in which to pamper my thinking processes with a little peace and quiet. In a short time I was ousted by the genial Canadian, Patrick Keatley, Commonwealth correspondent, who needed a home for his files. For the remainder of the *Guardian*'s stay at Gray's Inn Road I drew wherever I could find a free desk in the reporters' room, plywood drawing-board upon my knee.

The new Farringdon Road building promised great things — like a desk of one's own in the Features department. Came the big day I excitedly consulted the floor map and arrived at the appointed spot. Needless to say, there was nothing but carpet and a telephone point!

Interestingly, the area we had moved into, Clerkenwell, was credited with being the first place to record the name Gibbard, a variation on Gilbert, who came over with the Conqueror.

Having achieved my aim so early and so young, I spent my late twenties and early thirties in turmoil, worrying that the craft was obsolete, or that there was no future for Fleet Street. Twice I quit the *Guardian* for abortive new starts in New Zealand. One day, in gloomy mood, I attended an enchanting National Film Theatre lecture by John Halas, *Animal Farm* film-maker, marred only by the grim predictions he made for the future of full Disney-style animation. In no time I was enrolled at the London Film School learning the rudiments and shortly after joined Richard Williams (later to create and win Oscars for Roger Rabbit) in his studio at 13 Soho Square.

A great believer in throwing people in at the deep end, Dick promoted me to animator at a meteoric rate; but there were safety-nets about in the kindly and enthusiastic form of Hollywood old-timers — Grim Natwick, animator of Betty Boop and Snow White (who died recently after reaching the grand age of one hundred), Ken Harris (who I briefly assisted) who was Chuck Jones's top Bugs Bunny and Coyote animator, and the great animation teacher Art Babbit (responsible for the Wicked Queen in *Snow White*, Gepetto in *Pinocchio*, the mushroom and thistle dances in *Fantasia* and developer of Goofy). These great craftsmen were anxious that all should not be lost in the flood of Hanna Barbera limited animation and television cost-cutting and were delighted to hand on their secrets to enthusiastic youngsters.

British animation owes Dick Williams a great deal for luring these and other old masters to Soho to lecture or teach by example what has proved to be a magnificent new generation of fine young animators.

It struck me that the zest for life and constant observation of all its facets displayed by the great old animators contrasted mightily with the tired cynicism of not-so-old Fleet Street hacks. I made many pilgrimages to Hollywood and became a regular visitor to the Disney Studios, meeting great names from the past, recording their recollections and collecting their scribbles in my sketchbook. Frank Thomas, one of Disney's top Nine Old Men, urged me to marry two skills to produce animated political cartoons, a suggestion also made by Bob Clampett the early Warner Bros cartoon director.

It actually came to pass in 1976 when Granada Television gave the go-ahead for a regional politics programme using an eighteen-cartoon series called *Newshound*, featuring an old canine reporter who ponders the news over his pint.

These weekly two-minute spots were killers to produce, being animated between Thursday morning and Friday night with the assistance of another masochist who had also forsworn sleep in order to get things finished for the camera. There followed a Saturday-morning editing session, and after paying everyone off I usually pocketed £25. In spite of a growing fan club in the north the project proved too exhausting and I withdrew.

Channel Four's *A Week in Politics* also used animated sequences of my cartoons over a three-year period, but it always seemed a lot of hard work for a few fleeting seconds on the screen followed by oblivion.

The New Technology stampede began in Fleet Street. Eddie Shah gambled on a computerized *Today* and Rupert Murdoch despatched hundreds of old print craftsmen to the scrapheap en route to Fortress Wapping. The *Guardian* didn't intend to be left behind.

Ceilings at Farringdon Road were lowered for new air-conditioning. Floors were raised to take computer cables. The office was professionally redesigned so that it would look like any other City building, and things went eerily quiet as typewriters disappeared and staff abandoned conversation, mesmerized by their VDU screens.

We now had our very own presses in Docklands, and lo, the human eye could now decipher the half-tone pictures. This was a wonderful day for the long-suffering photographers who could at last hold their heads high. Their department now merited a bigger budget and gained substantial clout with an energetic new Picture Editor, the award-winning *Observer* photographer, Eammon McCabe. The pictures grew bigger and won more dramatic display, and the cartoon felt the squeeze.

In an attempt to halt the drain of readers to the newly established *Independent,* design consultants were called in to completely redesign the newspaper. Their conclusion was that photographs looked better with their new layouts than black-and-white drawing.

Instead of noisily barking at the world from the front lawn the cartoon was taken inside the house to the Parliament page. To those who have often asked why I haven't commented on recent history's most momentous events like the collapse of totalitarianism in Eastern Europe, the end of apartheid and the invasion of Kuwait by Iraq, the simple answer is that these events have had the temerity to occur during Parliamentary recess, when there is no page.

It's a peculiar fact that in days when the cartoon was plastered all over the front of the *Guardian* people who professed to being life-long readers of the paper would earnestly ask me where my cartoon appeared. Since the retreat inside, requests for originals have nearly trebled.

As New Technology was now all the rage, I leased a fax machine and moved out of town to rural bliss with my wife, two Irish wolfhounds, a black labrador and nine cats. The ghastly drives through the evening rush-hour to deliver artwork to an expressionless Night Editor were a thing of the past. Henceforth the cartoon would travel all by itself — along the lines of British Telecom.

In 1988 a new current-affairs flagship was being planned at BBC Television, the brainchild of John Birt (director-general in waiting), edited by another recruit from London Weekend Television and presented by Jonathan Dimbleby, also poached from ITV. *On the Record* had a healthy budget.

Could I draw some caricatures to illustrate a five-minute political commentary winding up the programme each week by John Cole, formerly of the *Guardian,* now the BBC's Political Editor. After further discussion the caricatures became political cartoons — seven or eight of them a week, thirty-eight weeks a year.

John and I neither met nor exchanged phone calls for several months. His script would arrive by messenger or fax, and he'd see my contributions only when he arrived at the studio.

When we did eventually meet at the Christmas party he admitted he was nervous that by so doing we might break the magic spell, but the partnership continues to gain in strength and captures a huge audience of luckless souls who tune in early for the Sunday edition of *Eastenders.* John deservedly co-won Broadcasting Journalist of the Year in 1991.

A background in animation has proved invaluable in drawing cartoons with camera moves in mind. Dreaming up eight ideas and drawing them in one Saturday afternoon is tough both mentally and physically, but a satisfying challenge.

*　　　　*　　　　*

As far as newspaper cartooning goes, I look forward to another two decades. I haven't yet been driven to Bill Papas's bottle of Scotch a day, although news does have a nasty habit of repeating itself just after you thought you'd said all there was to be said in a marvellous 'definitive statement'. The politicians become more manicured and processed, the policies more programmed and bland.

However, I persevere in the hope that somewhere outside a decent fish-and-chip shop that still wraps its fare in newspaper some eater will look hard at a greasy page of the *Guardian* of yesteryear and say: 'My, that really summed it all up!'

'I've always had the subconscious feeling that sooner or later someone is going to find me out and denounce me as an imposter who can't draw anyway,' Minhinnick wrote to me in 1976 when he received his knighthood. 'Now I am sure that exposure is imminent, and inevitably scorn and derision will follow. However, so far no one seems to have discovered the truth, so if you keep quiet about me, I'll keep mum about you, and we'll bluff our way through until the vulture critics pick our bones in the Never Never!' So far he's kept his word. Thanks, Min!